Twelve Cows
—AND WE'RE IN CLOVER

Twelve Cows
—AND WE'RE IN CLOVER

The Story of a Man Who Bought a Farm

With an Introduction by LOUIS BROMFIELD

By GEORGE REHM

NEW YORK

WILLIAM MORROW & COMPANY

1951

To RICHARD and BEA

Who Made So Much of This Book Possible

INTRODUCTION

THE PEOPLE OF THE UNITED STATES HAVE
more automobiles, more telephones, more plumbing, and
in general more mechanical conveniences and luxuries
than the rest of the world put together. The average
American knows a living standard in terms of material
things unrivalled by the people of any other nation. For
at least the last hundred years the average American has
believed that all of these things constituted happiness,
contentment and general satisfaction in life. It is only
recently, when even the shack along the railroad tracks
raises a complicated television receiving tower, that a
great many Americans have begun to have doubts.

In the past we have been inclined to mistake mere
change for progress and a restless activity for satisfactory
living. We rush from one part of the United States to
another and if we are rich enough, go on tours and visit
the peoples in other parts of the world. As a people and

as individuals we have a horror of ever being alone. We congregate constantly in conventions, at country clubs, in lodges and corner drugstores. In the past at least we have been the victims of a dynamism with very little direction and purpose beyond bigness and material achievement.

But within the past generation something curious has happened. People have become discontented and assailed by a feeling of emptiness and futility. They have become aware that the telephone can become a tyrant, that the automobile may possess and direct its owner, that noise and activity may merely be a means of marking time until we die. It may be that these are the first signs of maturity, signs that as a people we are beginning to grow up, and in gaining maturity we are discovering a sense of values which may bring about a real and a great civilization to which, as yet, we have no proper or valid claims. It may just be that we are discovering what all civilized people have always known—that mechanics do not constitute civilization, that machines are not in themselves the end but only a means to the end of giving man more time and more leisure for reflection, for an inner life, for thought and logic and a development of all the humanist virtues.

More and more people have turned away, not only from the noise and complexities of city life, but even from the convention and sterility of everyday American existence in the midst of telephones, automobiles, radios, plumbing and general empty hubbub. Many of these have made their exits into the country, either for good or, as in the case of many industrial workers, intellectuals and business men, on a part-time basis with an eventual and total escape in mind. I think the impulse arises from a strong instinctive sense of the superficiality and transience of a mechanical city existence in which time rushes by in a round of nerve-destroying complications. There is also a great impulse toward a more intimate contact with nature and natural law and in general with the universe and the laws which in the end govern man's existence down to the smallest details.

TWELVE COWS—AND WE'RE IN CLOVER is the record of the escape of one intelligent and sophisticated man together with his family . . . a man who knows the world and has "been everywhere." I make this point because he is both a typical and a symbolic case. Those who have sickened of our material luxury, of our mechanized existence, our razzle-dazzle morbidly gregarious society are rarely the stupid, the naïve or the inexperienced. They are usually those who know our modern society best and most profoundly. They have turned their backs and are seeking the deep satisfaction in living which is the birthright of every man and woman but which many of us never know at all.

The author of this book is not a crank, or a romantic or a visionary. He is a wise and experienced man who knows that he has a certain time in which to live and wishes to know something better than the country club, two cars in the garage, three bathrooms and radio-television antennae on every house.

This book is an engaging and charming one, reflecting the deep satisfaction of one man who in the middle of his life said to himself, "I have had enough nonsense. Now let's get down to real things." And at middle life he did not die suddenly of a heart attack because he had been persecuted too long by the monstrous demands of our mechanical civilization; he began living all over again and in the process became younger, physically stronger and wholly revitalized.

Like many another American in such circumstances, he was not the product of a farm or of rural life, yet the seeds were always there unrecognized until he began to suffer from the great American sickness of emptiness and materialism and looked about for an escape. He found it in the earth, in the landscape, in the cows, in the growing things, in matching his wits against the weather, in long evenings beside an open fire when in order to get through an evening great doses of whiskey and cocktails were unnecessary. In a sense he became again a man rather than a puppet and discovered satisfactions, very profound satisfactions, of which the average American is wholly ignorant. In a sense he became a three-dimensional person, such as no pure yokel or tenement dweller can ever be.

You can not help but like his enthusiasm for his new life and above all his understanding of animals and their closeness to us in almost every sense. As is the experience of every good dairyman, he discovered that every cow is a character and that very often they have more virtues than many people and, frequently enough, are infinitely more entertaining and lovable. The author is an experienced writer and that is always a help when it comes to making a book, for he is able to transfer to you his own satisfaction and even delight in taking a farm and its operation as his mission for the rest of his life. How many Americans have any mission or purpose at all beyond acquiring plumbing and automobiles? How

Introduction

many ever know the satisfaction that goes with a job of creation? It is something to think about.

The author does not give you a treatise on farming or running a dairy. We have hundreds of such articles and books, and dull reading they are. In a sense he has written an escape book which may be read by many people who will enjoy his own emotions and reactions vicariously . . . as if they themselves had shared the same experiences. TWELVE COWS is a sign, an omen and a symbol. A lot of Americans could read it to their advantage.

LOUIS BROMFIELD

CHAPTER 1

A LONG, LONG TIME AGO—ALL OF FOUR years—when I would shout what I prayerfully intended to be an imperious "Whoa!" to my mare Molly, I never knew just what would happen. Molly might halt in a trice, four feet spread and dug into the ground. She was equally capable of continuing her plodding gait, as though my stentorian command were a lost whisper. Now and then she executed a swift change into reverse that brought her rump almost onto my lap. Rarely did she take one or two easy steps and gently slow my seatless wagon to a halt which would leave me still upright on both feet, my cap on straight and the lines held with the careless assurance of a master horseman. In fact, a proper stop came so seldom that it was quite as disconcerting as her varied whimsies.

In those baptismal days of farming, Molly invariably outguessed me. If I braced for an abrupt halt, she would amble ahead most unconcernedly, even veering right or left for a tuft of clover, leaving me teetering like a brushed bowling pin. If I anticipated movement forward, she would halt, forcing me to my knees as the only way, humiliating or not, to remain aboard. When Molly abandoned all discipline and went into reverse, not even speedy genuflection could assure my continued presence on the wagon. It was so simple to pitch straight ahead onto the whiffletrees, with a frantic clutch at Molly's tail to keep me from the ground and the wagon rolling over me.

Those days, I trust, are ended. I survived largely because Molly is without malice and never took advantage of the plights she cast me into. A sardonic stare at me was sufficient satisfaction for Molly. Now, it is not very often that she catches me unawares. When I say "Whoa!" I am reasonably sure of achieving my idea of a three-point landing—both horses and the wagon stopping at the same time at a chosen spot. (Molly has been joined by a long-legged gelding, half her age of eighteen and paying constant obeisance to her seniority. Otherwise he gets severely nipped.) Winy triumph comes with a four-point landing, which bumps one wheel barely over a stone that will prevent the wagon from careening downhill when the horses are unhitched.

So after four years of farming, an outstanding achievement is that I can stand up most of the time. Nobody had ever hinted to me that equilibrium was a primary requirement for a city man trying to stay on a farm. No book ever informed me that I would be off-balance most of my waking moments for the first two years of my experiment with the land. But now I know. For months on end I never felt absolutely secure until I stretched out along the middle of a bed after reassuring myself that all four legs were solid. Even a chair held the menace of tipping unexpectedly.

The person raised on a farm never thinks twice about balance. He tromps about on a towering load of hay swaying across a rough field with all the nonchalance of an old sailing hand taking a reef in the top-royals while a gale pounds his ship. He steps about on a sloping barn roof with the aplomb of a riveter fastening girders on the fiftieth story of a skyscraper. Not so with me. I thought not only twice but a good twenty times before mounting a load of hay, some ten feet above ground level. As for the barn roof, when a leak had to be repaired instantly and no neighbor was handy to be cajoled into the job, I climbed the ladder rung by rung and in my stocking feet (somehow I felt better able to grip the inclined surface without shoes, though local experts grinned at me and declared shoes were better), I inched about, holding my breath when I peered over the edge at a thirty-foot drop, and wished devoutly my legs were much longer so that I could keep one braced against the ladder, which rose just above the roof hip.

I was uncomfortably aware that for too long a time I had been accustomed to city pavements, to uniform steps up and down, with a swaying subway car as the major opposition to my desire to stand erect. And even there a sturdy strap could be clung to to offset zooming curves and grinding stops. What a rapturous welcome I would have accorded a good subway strap as the last windrow cascaded onto the hay wagon and I caught it on my pitchfork, tossed it evenly to keep a square load, and trod it in the middle and along the edges, where the giddy sensation approximated that of an Alpine precipice, while the wagon tilted and jolted and rocked over stones and old furrows. Ah, for one small strap for just a few moments.

Take a mowing machine, horse-drawn, of course. With a tractor you sit in a capacious seat with a variety of levers and pedals for hand- or foot-holds, while the mower bounces along behind. But with horses for locomotion you sit on the mower at a nerve-tingling altitude of four feet, with nothing to hang on to and not much to brace the feet against. The machine is solid iron, with not a particle of spring to it. When one iron wheel bangs gratingly on a rock, that side of the mower rises, then drops with the most jarring thud you have ever experienced. Every jolt shortens the spine perceptibly so that after a few hours of cutting you feel of pygmy stature.

The Herculean task of staying put on the iron seat is complicated by several inescapable duties. The horses must be held to a straight line so that the cutting bar leaves an even swath; a switch must be used occasionally to keep the pace fast enough for clean cutting; the bar must be watched constantly so that it can be raised by a foot pedal when stones or mounds of gravel beside woodchuck holes menace the moving knives. The height of the bar from the ground must be maintained by a hand lever; the pitman bar, which drives the knives from wheel gears, must be guarded from stones high enough to strike it; and at least one eye must inspect the swathboard in case it gets clogged by the tall grass.

Thus about six pairs of eyes would be useful, also two

16

or three extra arms. But the mowing machine was unknown at the time of creation, and you get along with
the normal quota of two eyes and two arms and are
filled with wonderment that, somehow, you maintain
contact with the iron seat for a good fifty per cent of
the time.

Just as time was needed during World War II to acquire a "jeep seat," especially for a passenger without a
steering wheel to grip when the roads were pitted with
holes, so time brings triumph over the hazards of riding
on farm machinery. The reward is richly satisfying. I
recall no other feeling of victory comparable to that of
walking on a full load of hay as though it were the
kitchen floor, relaxing on a mowing machine as in a
rocker, or finding a three-legged milk stool a comfortable seat instead of a cranky contraption of Satan's.
Thus I have graduated from urban instability to rustic
equilibrium, though I was the only one to murmur "cum
laude" at the commencement exercises.

This kind of balance seems of vital importance at first,
the difference between life and a sudden demise. Later
it rates scant attention. Yet in gaining the one, a man
acquires other balances which are of deeper significance.
Farm life brings a balance between toil and leisure, sleep-
ing and waking, joy and despair. A physical balance
and a mental balance develop, taking their strength from
wind and rain, snow and ice and sunshine, from plants
that grow and die, from trees that burgeon and burgeon
again, from clean air and far-away hills and green meadows that turn brown but will surely be green again.
Death comes but life is close in its footsteps. The cycle
is an absolute because it is fundamental. Birth, growth,

death, decay—and the cycle begins again. It is on every side, and the countryman is a definite part of it, helping to complete the eternal but never wearisome round. And thereby he finds tranquillity.

Not that the country will bring serenity to every city person. Long familiarity with pavements, noise and crowds is not quickly changed. Silence and solitude can produce insanity as well as sanity. Not all farmers know this balance. Far too many of them struggle with the land as with an enemy, not a friend, and their minds are not at ease.

But those who want the country, after weighing its drawbacks, and who want it so ardently that they will toil cheerfully for its rewards will find security and peace. They will learn that every minor conquest fortifies the spirit. A new, laughing kind of self-confidence will begin to flourish. For balance is being achieved.

Any kind of farming can, with intelligence, produce this balance. The choice is a matter of preference. Thus far, dairying appeals to me as the pleasantest of all. Cows fit so perfectly into the cycle. They feed on grass and hay, they give milk in return, the manure goes to the fields to maintain the richness of the soil, so that more grass and hay will grow. In the early days a man with a cow was considered well off. The combination is still a sound one. The modern version is: ten cows provide a living; twelve cows put money in the bank. So, with a dozen cows at one end of the scale and one man, wobbly at first but holding fast, at the other, the beam gradually comes to rest and a new level of living is discovered.

Praise for any job well done is sweet music. When the boss claps you on the shoulder and speaks highly of you, your elation is boundless and for two or three days you wander in a rosy world. Yet never have I actually wallowed in triumph as I have since I became sole owner of a farm, a herd of cows and a horse. Unfamiliar tasks must be done no matter what the cost in sweat, ingenuity and discouragement. I am completely on my own, without someone at the adjoining desk or in the next office to consult. My nearest neighbor is a quarter-mile away. So it is up to me regardless of how very much alone I feel. When those odds are surmounted triumph has real meaning.

In August, 1947, after nearly thirty years in Europe, I returned to the United States with my wife Mary and sixteen-year-old son John, better known as Scoop. I was fifty-three. Service with the Psychological Warfare Branch of the Office of War Information had taken me, in October, 1942, to England on a hush-hush trip by air, then by convoy to Algiers for the Allied landings in November, to Tunis, Sicily and Italy as far north as Florence, then to France for the southern Invasion and finally to Paris. During a brief leave in New York in the winter of 1944-45, when the outcome of the war was assured and psychological warfare superfluous against an enemy already demoralized, I decided to continue with the peace-time counterpart of O.W.I., the United States Information Service, a State Department innovation in international affairs. The prospect of using information (propaganda, if you like, but truthful propaganda) to improve relations around the world was stimulating after two wars that had only increased bitterness and animosity.

I returned to Paris, drove a station wagon loaded with material to Marseilles and there, in the city known as the "Communist stronghold of France," set up an information service, with a small local staff. Through media such as documentary films, pamphlets, articles for newspapers and items for the radio, plus a good lending library, I tried to spread a better picture of the United States and its citizens, a picture naturally at great variance with impressions instilled by the Nazis and later by the Communists.

The work was extremely interesting, of genuine value and sorely needed. Human nature being what it is, slanderous statements always gain credence over praise. I discovered the most fantastic yarns being repeated as sober fact; news items were wildly distorted and still found people to believe them, particularly among workers and peasants. To encounter this in France, a truly enlightened country, was disturbing, to say the least, and it was not hard to imagine how much more troubling the problem would be in the Balkan countries, in the Near East and in the Orient.

Nevertheless, in the spring of 1947, Congress voted to reduce sharply the budget for U.S.I.S., including the Voice of America. The Marseilles bureau was one of many that had to be closed for lack of funds. I could have continued somewhere else with U.S.I.S., or joined with UNESCO. I might have resumed newspaper work, which had furnished my livelihood in Europe between World Wars I and II. On the other hand, this was the moment to make a decision I had been pushing aside for some time: to continue living in Europe to doddering old age or to get back home to a feeling of permanency instead of the transient one that had never been completely allayed in France or other parts of Europe.

The idea of farming had long been in the back of my mind, very alluring at times, rather terrifying when examined in clear light. Suddenly it became commanding, the one solution. The land offered the permanency I desired. All other plans became futile, like shining up old shoes to make them look new, or warming up Sunday leftovers. Farming promised adventure.

One point must be made clear. I was not disillusioned with the world, I was not soured on humanity. I was not prompted by any urge to "get away from it all." City life and work had not given me ulcers or increased my blood pressure by a single point. I liked people and took great pleasure in such urban advantages as the theater, music and art galleries. In short, I was in fine fettle, with no sizable quarrels with anyone. But I still wanted to try farming.

For a brief interval I was tempted to make my agricultural debut in France, in the Var Department, which I came to know intimately while headquartered in Marseilles. I like France and, after Paris, I have a special fondness for Provence. The Var region of Provence is a rugged country of limestone crags and deep gorges, with scattered sweeps of level plains and fields. The past and the present merge happily there, walk arm in arm, aware of momentous happenings that portend drastic changes, yet secure in an age-old experience which teaches that light-heartedness never should be forsaken no matter how ominous the outlook. The people possess an innate gaiety that overrides worry and dark forebodings, an exuberance that must be a heritage from the troubadours.

The Neapolitan is the only other I know who is similarly gifted. Both can burst into carefree song when the situation is at its direst.

The Var country, like its people, is somber and joyous, disturbing and soothing, mirroring one's moods and temperament. I have two paintings done at approximately the same place in the Var. One is by René Seyssaud, more than eighty years old and still called, with Provençal pride, the living Cézanne. Seyssaud is Catholic, with a quick laugh, twinkling eyes, a youthful spirit age cannot dim. His canvas is rich with color, vibrant, warm as the Var earth in June. André Chabaud, who joined with the *Fauves* in his youth in Paris, painted the other. He is an austere Protestant, a true Huguenot, working his farm as his ancestors did when he is not painting. His picture is gray, chill, stern. The few flecks of red flowers seem to have been dabbed on against his will. Sharply contrasting, both pictures are unmistakably the Var.

Here was country that I found most satisfying, from its inland plains, fragrant with wild thyme and lavender, to the pine-covered slopes that dropped into the Mediterranean, that seductive body of blue water. The Var had appealed to me when I first took a walking trip through Provence in 1921 and its appeal had broadened and strengthened as acquaintanceship developed into intimacy. Moreover, my affection for the region was at its peak when my post in Marseilles was terminated, so that temptation was strong to acquire a piece of land and dig in there for all time.

I had made many friends during the sojourn in Marseilles, even during a brief stay in the region after landing at St. Tropez in August, 1944, for the belated invasion of southern France. Firm friends they were, too, with both the sparkle and indolence of the Mediterranean and Provençal climate. They were painters, writers, journalists, professors, French government men, many of them poor or of modest means. But every one had a marvelous zest for living. The prospect of a quiet existence in the country, interrupted occasionally by festive nights in Marseilles, was not easy to put aside.

Many of my friends occupied themselves strenuously with the search for a farm that would meet my few requirements, for in rural southern France you just don't expect much by way of modern conveniences. I could have spent several weeks in a car visiting properties that were discovered for me, near Aix-en-Provence, St. Tropez, even Draguignan. I never did get to Draguignan, even to say good-bye, and I regret missing the occasion to recall an incident there soon after our combat group landed and started north.

A collaborationist newspaper was promptly suppressed in Draguignan when we arrived close on the heels of American troops, who could roll fast because the way had been cleared by the thoroughly organized French resistance movement. The owner of the printing establishment was eager to revive his pre-Occupation journal and when details such as news sources, paper, and the like had been agreed upon, he proposed a gala dinner.

Peter Rhodes, also in Psychological Warfare, and I knew it would be as much of a banquet as could be achieved after two years of German occupation—the last bit of sugar, tins of pâté de foie gras and other luxuries treasured for the day of liberation, and probably the last rabbit or chicken that had been secreted from the Germans. So we did some scrounging to contribute our share. It amounted to only a few C rations, candy bars and cigarettes, except for a fifty-pound sack of American white flour. We took into our confidence the wife of our host; she found a baker, and a quantity of real, golden, crusty French *petits-pains* was baked the afternoon of the dinner. The baker took his payment in kind and was in raptures.

After glasses of white wine for cocktails, Peter and I sat down with ten French men and women. Hors d'oeuvres were in sumptuous variety, for everyone had dug up a tin or two of tidbits. Then "Occupation bread," a dark, soggy, wholly unappetizing product which the French cursed, was passed. Apologies were profuse for such an ignoble imitation of bread. Suddenly our hostess appeared and set on the table a basket filled with the elongated rolls, exactly the same as before the war.

The guests gaped incredulously at the heaping basket. They tried to speak but words were beyond utterance. Some frowned suspiciously, believing it was an ill-conceived hoax and the rolls made of paper for a window display. One more trusting guest finally seized a roll, broke it gingerly as though it might explode. It crackled invitingly; the interior was white and fragrant. At once, arms reached from all directions, with no thought of formal table manners. Gasps of astonishment were the only sound. Pieces were broken off, chewed, swallowed. Each person stared round-eyed at his neighbor. Then came the flood of words. From there on it was the gayest dinner I have ever attended. Several men and women scorned practically everything else on the menu. They munched bread, impervious to jibes and quips.

These same people, three years later, made every effort to find a farm for me. They would have been good neighbors—as so many others like them would have been. Regarded on the bright side, the outlook was most alluring. And for a brief moment I saw myself and wife and son ensconced in an old stone house with as much land as could be bought, in view of the inflated values that still prevailed, producing almost all, if not all, our food and living fully as the people of Provence know so well how to do.

But it was a brief moment. The other side of the picture was shadowed by many handicaps. They probably could have been overcome for the most part, but I soon realized that there would be a void in the undertaking, even if it were successful. I had thrived for many years in France, yet I had never felt completely at home. No roots had really taken hold. Owning a farm in France would lend a sense of permanency but I knew it would be superficial, even false, and that always I would feel that I was fundamentally a stranger. The answer was plain. What I needed was earth that was my own by right of birth as well as right of purchase.

Here was an abrupt change in personal viewpoint. After thirty years of footloose living, during which the suggestion of a trip to new places had been immediately embraced and made a reality, the nomadic blood had suddenly run thin. The swing had been complete. One manner of living had ended, in one of its pleasantest phases, and another, still vague in outline, was about to begin. Yet vagueness could not alter the inexorability of the urge. It just had to be.

No more bullfights in the ancient Roman arena at Nîmes, in the genial company of Ambrogiani, a Corsican painter in Marseilles who lives as boldly as he paints. No more five-hour lunches with Leon Mouche, program director for Radio Marseilles and an inexhaustible source of information and anecdote on art, music, literature or, perhaps, a young *vin rosé* discovered near Aix. No more swims in the crystal waters of the Mediterranean; no more fishing for sea urchins and devouring the catch at once with swabs of bread and dry white wine. No more excursions to Les Baux with its ruins of a feudal castle that was the center of Provence when Queen Jeanne held her courts of love; to the Abbaye de Mont Major; to the haunts of Van Gogh and Cézanne in nearby Arles; to Aiguesmortes, that fantastic pile of stone whence Saint Louis set forth on the last crusade. No more *menades* or round-ups of young fighting bulls on the salt marshes near Les Martigues, where the bulls are bred and raised, a genial, noisy carousing with the local absinthe, called *pastis*, cauldrons of fish stew and slabs of broiled bull steak. No more communing with criminals, petty and big-time, in bars surrounding the Marseilles opera, a juxtaposition typical of the seaport that dates back to the Phoenicians . . .

It was to be farewell to all this and a thousand other diversions that cram the Provençal calendar. Two years in Marseilles had provided a memorable climax to more than half a lifetime in Europe. Not since the early 1920's in Paris had such a brief interval encompassed so much exuberant living. I am glad the end came at that moment, swiftly, as though a bright, sharp blade had neatly severed the past while it was sparkling, fresh, before a trace of staleness could mar its spontaneity.

Departure brought regrets, but they were dulled by the overpowering urge to get back home and find that farm. One cup had been filled pretty much to the brim. I had wandered as I had pleased, known new lands, learned new languages, met new people. Now another cup waited to be filled, a rustic one, more of the plain old tin kind, but its magic was every bit as potent as the first. And it still is.

CHAPTER 2

Scoop and i set out in the car early in September, 1947, to find the farm—not *a* farm but *the* farm—that possessed all the practical essentials demanded by my collection of books on farming, plus as many esthetic values as we would be lucky enough to find. The esthetic aspect of the farm was important to us but secondary to the practical, whereas it appeared to be primary in my wife's conception, for at no time can it be said that she waxed lyrical over gaining a livelihood from the soil, far from the people, the theaters and all the other trappings of a modern city. She acquiesced to the venture only after voicing an array of misgivings and pointing out a multitude of drawbacks, some of which have all too literally proved true. But at the start, esthetics were mainly a sop to my spouse.

The two of us toured part of Delaware, part of Maryland and eastern Pennsylvania, from south to north. I had barred New Jersey because of a prejudice which I do not even attempt to analyze, as I know very little of the state. The prejudice is there and is determined to stick. New York State likewise had a mark against it for some equally unaccountable reason. Delaware and Maryland were soon eliminated because of their sticky summers and dank winters. Previously, Vermont and New Hampshire had been crossed off the list because the winters there were too severe and long. Connecticut was considered too much of a backyard-frontyard for New York City.

Thus we found ourselves concentrating on eastern Pennsylvania with the exception of Bucks County, where farms were sure to be well above our maximum price level. We traveled from town to town, discussing our project with independent real-estate men or agents of the big farm-listing companies. There seemed to be little choice between the two types of salesmen. The smallest dealer, with a tiny cubicle for an office and only one shabby chair for customers, was quite as likely to know of an idyllic spot such as I had in mind as the agent with imposing quarters and a whole drawerful of farms for sale. Our aim was to visit all the dealers we could locate and, after considerable sifting, decide on two or three farms that promised results. It was a long, slow, discouraging job. Again and again we found our hopes raised by the itemized description of a farm, a strictly factual presentation, only to have them slump during the first five minutes of inspection.

But we kept wheeling along, gradually working north, getting accustomed to low spirits at night and a matutinal resurgence of courage, sufficient for the morning but ebbing fast by mid-afternoon. We learned that the first thing to discover about a prospective farm was the reason for its being sold. Sometimes a direct question would bring a prompt reply that had an honest ring. When we met with hesitation or evasiveness, we were prepared for drawbacks, to the point of not bothering to drive to the place. What had forced the owner to sell probably would suffice to bring us to a similar decision after a brief trial.

Eventually just two causes for disposal aroused our immediate interest. We came to beam ghoulishly when informed that death or illness compelled the sale. One or the other bid fair to indicate that the farm was still in good condition and that only an act of God prevented the owners from continuing on the same piece of land.

Late in September we rolled into northeastern Pennsylvania and Susquehanna County. We agreed that the countryside was most pleasing. Hills and valleys forked off in all directions, streams seemed to flow in every valley, lakes and ponds were frequent. Wooded ridges looked much as they had to the roaming Delawares. There were no cities close enough to be disturbing, and many of the villages had an air of quiet pride and thriftiness. The farms, moreover, were generally attractive and in good repair—going concerns that sometimes were obviously prosperous. There was more pull, more allure to the region than any we had been through.

Our hopes rose once again, agents were found in villages, farms were discussed and visited. And one day the present High Meadows emerged at the end of a dirt road and a short lane leading to a compact group of house, barn, sheds and poultry houses. Fields lay close to the house; beyond them were wooded slopes, except to the west where the view extended for several miles along and across valleys to more tree-crowned ridges. The setting possessed an intimate quality, inviting one to sit down and rest and gaze leisurely at the landscape. It offered solitude but not loneliness, perhaps because of two or three white farmhouses glimpsed among trees a mile or more distant. And as it gave off friendliness, I returned it in excessive measure.

It wasn't a model farm by any means. Its faults were many. But it had been an operating unit under one family name for more than fifty years. The father had willed it to his eldest son. Two other sons had been given adjoining farms and so, as neighbors, still maintained a genuine interest in the homestead. The eldest son had died and his widow, left with young children, had been unable to continue farming. She had returned to schoolteaching and offered the farm for sale. Until a buyer was found the place had been rented to a nephew. As a result, the fields had been cultivated up to the time I arrived. In fact, one nine-acre meadow and another of five acres displayed a seeding of clover so lush that even my urban eyes could appreciate its richness.

This background was auspicious, in view of our previous experience. The farm, with its cluster of buildings and surrounding fields, had personality, like a solid citizen with a sense of humor and a little money in the bank. There were, moreover, esthetic values—a panorama to the west with a horizon sufficiently distant to complement a sunset, magnificent trees, old stone walls, and a brook roaring or trickling over great boulders and

31

ledges. Nevertheless, we made no decision. A few other prospects remained on our list, and we dutifully continued on our way while I tried vainly to smother worries that someone else might buy the place before I returned. In all truth I got back to High Meadows as fast as I could.

I am not sure whether a curb should be put on such an immediate attachment for a desired object. The possibility of a better buy always exists, and the prudent procedure is to continue investigating to the very end. Yet when meadows and woods and buildings all speak to you with one voice and a bond is established in an instant between you and a particular piece of land, then perhaps you might as well accept destiny, for better and worse, and forget other chance discoveries. You may let yourself in for disappointments but, in return, you will not be saddled with regrets. Had I come upon another farm with certain advantages over this one, I would have been beset by interminable comparisons, which do not make for peace of mind. As it was, no other farm I had seen could rival it and I enjoyed the very pleasant feeling of having found exactly the place I wanted. So I bought it, as though I were in a great hurry. Such satisfaction was a great prop to faltering courage when shortcomings appeared, as they did later, and I wondered how I had ever overlooked them.

The farm can be briefly described. It comprises 155 acres, thirty-three of which are tillable, the balance being in woods and unimproved pasture, the latter a section I intend to experiment with in order to raise the quality and quantity of grazing growth. In addition to the house and barn, and the phantom silo, there are two chicken

houses, a small machinery shed and a larger shed which now houses my car, the bunnies and, in the loft, the pigeons. The pigpen I built later.

The asking price was $6,500, including livestock, some old machinery, and a third interest in still other machinery which I would share with the two surviving brothers whose farms were adjoining. The machinery was enough to start with, but some venerable pieces, like the mower, have since been replaced by my own purchases. Pooch, a cat, likewise decided to come with the farm. She deserted my neighbors, Richard and Bea, who had called her Boots because she has seven toes on each front foot, and moved in with me the day I arrived, a kind of friendly gesture I appreciated but was at a loss to explain. In those early days I had little time to give her, but she stayed and now is a grandmother at High Meadows.

I have never been a good bargainer, and when something I want appeals to me I am quite incapable of haggling over a price. I had read in books that the asking price of a farm should be regarded as one-third higher than the price that will be accepted. I strove earnestly to keep this in mind, but I am afraid my enthusiasm for the farm was poorly concealed. The agent countered my lower bids with lengthy, documented arguments to prove that they were unacceptable, indeed nothing short of an insult to the farm's true value. When I finally managed a reduction of $250 I felt I had gained a real victory. Unquestionably someone more adept in bargaining and with a better poker-face could have obtained a greater reduction. Nevertheless, I was far from

cheated and still feel satisfied with the sum of $6,250 eventually agreed upon.

As I wanted to have a fair amount of cash on hand for expenses during the first year, I arranged a $2,000 mortgage with a local bank. This was my first experience with a mortgage, and at the outset I could scarcely suppress memories of the hard-hearted mortgage-holders I had encountered in Horatio Alger books. The banker soon dispelled such alarms, however, and I now count the country or village bank as a great institution. The president knows the countryside intimately; he is full of wise council and sound advice and will be surprisingly understanding and lenient when mishaps interfere temporarily with payments on loans. He is part of the land almost to the same degree as the farmer, appreciating the many adversities that may occur. If he feels that the intent is good, he will bear uncomplainingly with valid excuses.

Nevertheless, the banker I dealt with has admitted that he is not always the judge of character he pretends to be. The story came out months after I had first met him, when the "Mister" stage was giving way to the first-name status. I met him, with the lawyer who had handled the legal details of the purchase, at a farm auction. As usual the lawyer felt my hands for callouses, laughed when he found sizable ones and turned to the bank president.

"You see? Admit you were wrong."

"All right. I do. But don't rub it in."

Then he told me the story. When I first appeared at the bank, he decided I was, in his own words, the "poorest gamble" as a potential farmer he had ever met.

However, since the farm and livestock were more than sufficient security, he determined to grant the mortgage anyway. But he also made a bet with the lawyer that I would not last six months . . . Now the lawyer, who backed me in the bet, never misses an occasion to remind the banker how great was his error and make him apologize for it. In fact friendship among us is now on such a firm basis that I can rib the banker himself about it, especially when he comes into my barn and admits that the cows look fine and obviously show good care.

On one other point, however, he declares he has never been wrong and I am willing to agree with him. When an embryonic farmer comes to him for a mortgage, he asks to meet the wife, if there is one. And with only half an ear for the big ideas and hopes of the man, he manages to extract the opinions of the wife on farming, living in the country, the handicaps involved, the loneliness and the self-reliance demanded. Not until he is sure of her attitude does he like to discuss financial matters. And there he is on solid ground, for it is much more likely that the woman will be the first to find initial ardor cooling to open dislike, with abandonment of the farm as the only solution.

The decision to buy High Meadows made, Scoop returned for his senior year at school in New York, where my wife took a small apartment. From the start we had agreed that I would face the first winter alone. I vastly preferred going through my initiation period without an audience to note my mistakes and blunders. So I found a village hotel a few miles from the farm and slept there while details of a clear title, payments and other business were being completed. Whenever possible

I spent hours, whole days, at the farm which I already called mine though I could not move in until final papers were signed. I desired nothing more than to sit on the house porch in the sun and visualize next year's crops in nearby fields, chickens in one shed, rabbits in another, pigeons in a loft. Everything was wonderful, life was full—not a weed in sight, not a mishap in the whole vista. Lunacy is the only stage beyond such a roseate condition but I paid no heed. All I craved was more of that October sunshine, with a gauzy haze caught in the brilliant hues of the trees, and a surfeit of dreams.

I came briefly to my senses, obliged to confess humbly that I was still a city man, during an excursion with my neighbor's son, who had agreed to show me the boundaries of the farm, the peripheral line of stone wall and barbed wire which, with frequent gaps, separated my world from everything beyond.

I had long entertained the conviction that I was completely at home in the great outdoors. As a boy I had camped, fished, hunted, studied woodcraft with great zeal, read Stewart Edward White with passionate attention. During the many intervening years, I maintained that I had not lost any of my youthful skill in cruising through woods and fields. But I failed to reckon with the numerous pounds of excess flesh acquired after forty, muscles no longer supple for lack of use, and the fact that I was wearing city clothes and shoes, the soles of the latter becoming as slippery as a greased pole when I trod on leaves and moss and ferns.

My guide set a moderately fast pace, perhaps accelerated a trifle just because I was from the city. I kept up as best I could, determined to prove that the city had removed but little of my former adeptness in the wilds. Conversation, fortunately, was limited to occasional explanatory remarks that required little more than a grunt of understanding, for I was shortly in a breathless state that forbade uttering a complete sentence without explosive gasps for air.

After winding through a section of sugar bush, with many lofty maples that had survived the blight that had swept through the region, we plunged into a dense growth of hemlock that engulfed my companion like a heavy curtain. I floundered on, unsnagging my jacket from branches, tripping over branches, grabbing for my glasses as low branches swept them askew. I felt very far removed from that Indian, Deerfoot, whose effortless and silent course through thick woods I had at one time almost equalled.

Suddenly I almost stumbled into the arms of my guide. He was standing on the edge of an outcropping of rock that fell away sheer for ten feet or more, the land beyond running sharply down as a steep floor for close-growing beeches, black birches, elms and hickories. Sun through the leaves cast a greenish light that seemed almost as liquid as though I were submerged in water. The spot was completely primeval, as lost to civilization as it had been a hundred years before or ten thousand years. At a more propitious moment I would have peered stealthily about for a glimpse of Deerfoot's swarthy countenance.

My companion was saying something about the boundary line being off to the left and that we would pick it up again down below. I leaned forward to follow the wave of his arm, my urban footgear slithered uncontrollably on mossy rock, and just like that I was plummeting

37

to the ground at the foot of the small cliff. I landed flat on my side, bounced like a sodden softball and emitted an echoing grunt as what little air remaining in me was expelled in one swift puff. I got to my feet, unhurt in body but bitterly wounded in mind by such a demonstration of city ineptitude. I remember mumbling a kind of plaintive apology for such awkwardness, as much as to say that as a rule I did much better. But my friend was so relieved to be assured that I was alive and perfectly sound that he had no thought for clumsiness or a snicker of enjoyment over my mishap. In fact, he was most solicitous for the remainder of the trip, though not until we were much better acquainted was I able to laugh about it without any trace of embarrassment.

A few days later the final formalities at the bank were signed and sealed, and on October 28, 1947, I took possession of my bucolic abode. Pending arrival of furniture still in storage, the house boasted a kitchen table and two old chairs, one decrepit armchair and a bed. There was a coal range in the kitchen plus a few cracked dishes and a frying pan. I had loaded the car with groceries, dried and canned staples, a ham, a slab of bacon and some fresh meat. Enough coal remained in the cellar to fire the range. I purred and burbled to myself, enveloped in welcome heat from the stove, while I prepared asparagus on toast with melted butter, broiled T-bone steak, raw fried potatoes, salad, cheese and cherry pie. I had also provided a jug of wine, and the wine and the food made a sumptuous repast. Thus I waved a joyous farewell to hotel and restaurant fare, and rarely since then have I returned to it.

Between courses I could not resist wandering from

room to room—dining room, living room, a downstairs bedroom that soon became a library, four upstairs bedrooms and a bathroom. A ramshackle summer kitchen off the kitchen. A big cellar with a hot-air furnace that functioned despite its age. A roofed porch to the south, toward the barn, and to the east, facing the lane. Spring water pumped electrically to the house into a pressure tank whence it served the kitchen, bathroom and barn. A coal, "bucket-a-day" water-heater in the cellar. And electric light throughout house and barn . . . The house itself was plain, without a single line that could be called charming. It was in desperate need of paint outside and decoration inside to obliterate dark woodwork and prevailing somberness. But it was a house, it was mine, and for the moment I refused to recognize a single flaw that could not be easily remedied.

CHAPTER 3

SUBSISTENCE FARMING WAS THE BRANCH OF
agriculture to which I had proposed to dedicate my remaining years. I had devoted a good deal of time to
books on the subject, and to a semi-somnolent state in
which I viewed myself as a neo-pioneer producing an
excellent living by my hands and a brain which I was
pleased to regard as better equipped than the old-time
pioneer's for managing the project. At any moment of
leisure I could immediately summon up a distinct and
detailed picture of myself quietly and purposefully pur-
suing my round of daily duties and experiments so fruit-
ful in their achievement that by evening I could say, with
a self-satisfied air one jump short of smug, that I had
won all the needs and comforts essential to my well-
being. As I have long been one who likes good food, to
the extent of considering myself a gourmet of modest
stature, my needs and comforts centered mainly on the
larder.

Subsistence farming means obtaining from the land by one's own toil and skill as nearly everything as possible required for maintaining body and soul in reasonably close contact. I visualized them in flourishing and intimate harmony, with the body getting the major share of sustenance.

By my own visionary hands I produced hams and bacons redolent of smoke from green black-birch chips; sausage meat, seasoned with home-grown sage, put down in crocks and covered with lard; old-fashioned liver sausage to accompany homemade sauerkraut; head cheese; genuine, not "boughten" scrapple; an ample supply of fresh pork fattened on clover and corn. Chickens clucked contentedly in my barnyard, assuring meat and eggs; a few ducks and geese ambled about, if I craved a richer diet. Squabs gaped hungrily in a shed loft; guinea hens reminded me raucously that they made delectable eating. A cow generously supplied all my milk and cream as well as butter. (In those days of dreaming, that lone cow was my nearest approach to dairying.) My bossy also produced annually a calf to be raised for veal, liver, broiled veal kidneys, sweetbreads, or, after a couple of years of good feeding, a baby beef for choice steaks, roasts and stews, plus, among innumerable other dishes, fresh tripe for *tripes a la mode de Caen,* one of my favorite concoctions.

These gustatory meanderings set off chain reactions that ended only when I lapsed into full slumber or a telephone aroused me to the fact that I had to work for a living in an office building, not on the land. Tripe, for instance, demanded cider and *calvados,* or applejack. So, in my self-sufficiency, I had to make cider, allowing a cask of the beverage to harden, then to freeze solidly, when the highly alcoholic core would be removed by ramming a red-hot poker through the frozen exterior. Beer and wine at once came to mind and with equal speed were provided from the hops I would grow and the grapevines I would prune religiously, as I had seen them pruned along the Cote d'Or in Burgundy.

I recall—in fact, the idea haunts me frequently now I am on a farm—that I finally narrowed down the items I would be compelled to purchase to tea, coffee, salt, pepper, other spices and the few clothes and shoes I would need. I dwelt for a time on sheep as providers of wool which I could weave into beautiful coarse tweeds, but that vision faded at the spinning-wheel stage. The garden, naturally, would provide all my vegetables, fresh, canned and dried; the orchard and the fields would solve my fruit problem—berries wild and tame for jam; a currant jelly, perchance, to accompany venison or squirrel or even pheasant, all of which would fall before my gun each hunting season.

Sugar? A few hives of bees would give me honey which, books told me, was better than sugar, even in coffee. I must try it some day. Hard maple trees, moreover, offered sugar and syrup, the latter crying for buckwheat cakes. Buckwheat flour? I would grow buckwheat, grind it as needed. Wheat flour, too. Genuine, unadulterated whole wheat flour for crusty bread. I fretted for a long while about olive oil, finally admitting that the best solution would be to drop pointed hints to friends and relatives before Christmas and so amass as much as a gallon of it. For general use, on the other hand, I would grow soy beans and press my own cooking oil, as the Chinese do.

Such dreams are not entirely sheer fantasy. They can be realized, every one of them. They have been, if books are truthful. But the person who does merits extravagant praise. There just aren't enough hours in the day if you are alone and succumb occasionally to an urge to sit down and rest. Also, the temptation to compromise on just a few items beyond salt and spices is well nigh irresistible. Then compromise expands; you convince yourself that a few tinned items will mean only a temporary lapse, until the rigid principle of subsistence farming is warped and twisted to embrace much that is so convenient and cheap it would be absurd to waste time producing it.

I still feel pangs of guilt when I look at my shelves of canned goods and purchased edibles. But I don't make much headway toward altering the situation. Occasionally I feel wasteful when I wash my hands and remember that years ago I intended to make my own soap. Such feelings, however, are fleeting. I am certain I will never make soap, even as an experiment.

Nevertheless, I salve my conscience with the knowledge that I have fulfilled some of those dreams. I do smoke my own hams and bacon, make sausage, provide my own veal. But I buy my steaks and roasts. I have quantities of milk and cream, yet I sell it and buy my butter. I pay for my wine because actually it is cheaper than to buy real wine grapes (which do not grow well in my countryside) and make my own, and in the long run it is of better quality. As for bread, I have a neighbor who bakes as good bread as possible with American

43

bolted and processed flour. Only if I had to eat the usual store loaf would I feel obliged to grind my flour and bake my bread.

One thing is sure: subsistence farming is feasible. Given sufficient capital to pay expenses for the first year, until production can be organized and markets assured, a livelihood is almost guaranteed for the single man or the family that prefer to work in the country and are willing to work assiduously. If they are good bargainers and traders they can even assure themselves a modest cash income over and above their own food requirements and so be able to pay for clothes and other general expenses.

Nevertheless, I am most grateful to the destiny that steered me from subsistence farming and into dairying.

As I have said, I am a poor bargainer, either at arguing down a seller's price or holding out for my own. There is no pleasure for me in making a game out of it as the Oriental does. To him, the battle of wits, the mental swordplay, is quite as fascinating as the money involved. He is insulted if his opening price, outrageously high, is accepted, for the game is cut short at its very beginning. But something of that Eastern attitude is required if you peddle your produce to townfolk—always a more profitable practice than exchanging it for goods at local stores. You must have tact and patience, together with a temperament impervious to petty fault-finding and hard-luck yarns. Bills must be collected; customers must be dunned if profit is to be made.

I am not heavily endowed along these lines. Nevertheless, during the period when subsistence farming was my bright hope, I struggled valiantly to persuade myself that I could nurture a spindly commercial instinct to stalwart growth and be a shrewd salesman if need be. That evolution remains highly doubtful and in any case I wouldn't have been very happy about it.

There is, however, a newly developed method for disposal of one's produce which eliminates all personal dealings. Public sales have recently been organized in rural districts where, the boast is, anything submitted for auction will be sold, from a bundle of rags to a truckload of apples. Dealers and commission men attend these sales, along with hotelkeepers, restaurant owners and housewives. Prices generally are comparable with city market quotations, particularly for current produce such as poultry, eggs, livestock and vegetables. The sales organization takes a small commission and the balance goes to the producer. I have found the system thoroughly satisfactory for selling bull calves, old machinery, even such miscellany as a bushel of hickory nuts. It is, moreover, an economical way of buying a sack of potatoes, a young porker to fatten or whatever else is needed, as the price is wholesale.

At one time I also weighed the merits of crop farming, but abandoned it after some study. Primarily, I was bothered by the prospect of working for months or a whole year to produce crops that would have to be sold when harvested, just when most other farmers were selling and prices were necessarily at their lowest point. I foresaw little likelihood of being in a position to store grain or beans or potatoes over a considerable period until prices were at their peak.

Another aspect of the financial side of crop farming was unprepossessing. For approximately the entire first year, there would be little, if any, cash return, and money would, therefore, have to be set aside to meet expenses during those many months. Some bills could be allowed to accumulate on the strength of coming harvests, but that would mean that a sizable portion of the annual income would be gobbled up as soon as it arrived, thus diminishing the capital earmarked for the forthcoming twelve months and reviving the bogey of more bills piling up. I came to feel extremely uncomfortable at the thought of facing creditors, no matter how sympathetic, for endless weeks without a possibility of paying them. Discomfort, however, turned to acute mental agony when it occurred to me that a series of meteorological accidents might ruin all or a big share of my crops, thereby wiping out income, thereby increasing debts and thereby compelling me to quit.

The amount of work for one man demanded by crop farming likewise received some long pondering. To produce harvests big enough to cover expenditures over a whole year would mean plowing, harrowing, seeding and cultivating a lot of acres. A tractor and its accompanying machinery would shorten the job but such machinery costs a sizable sum of money, more than I cared to hazard at the very outset. Horses were the alternative. Never having plowed in my life, never having harnessed a horse, I was unable, in my most bemused moments, to persuade myself that I could cope with forty acres of tillable land, the very minimum according to my calculations.

For a while I clung optimistically to someone's estimate that five acres could be plowed in a day with a team of horses. Later I learned, more reliably, that two acres made a good daily average, quite sufficient to leave me bone-weary when I headed for the barn. Thus twenty days of good weather would be devoted to plowing; harrowing would go at a slightly faster clip; then the grain drill, faster still. Since plowing could rarely start before the middle of April, with a certain amount of time lost because of bad weather, I saw myself still planting seeds well along in June; and even as a city dweller, I knew that corn ought to be knee-high by the Fourth of July.

Against this dismal outlook I posed the pleasanter aspect of long summer days watching the crops grow and ripen, also the long winter with virtually nothing to do. To be sure, the livestock would have to be fed and watered, and I generously included a few odd jobs, "tinkering" in local parlance. Nevertheless, many hours would remain in every day for reading and dozing in a big chair in a warm room while winter ruled just beyond the frosty windowpanes. It was precisely the kind of chromo found on country calendars, even to the dog snoozing at my feet. The vision of snug repose, however, was monotonously interrupted by the specter of spring. No longer did it loom ahead as a season of joy and festival when nature shrugged out of her dormant state and the earth donned a fresh, green frock. Only forced labor would lie ahead of me, with unpaid bills as a knout to flail me from dawn till dark. Viewed in that realistic light, crop farming soon lost all its allure.

My attitude toward work is simply defined. I am willing to work hard when I must, but I am not the type with an inner, feverish drive that stays in top gear every waking hour. There is nothing hyper about my thyroids.

47

I have a great and constant love of leisure. Though not innately lazy, I am ever ready to sit down for a smoke or a chat or just to gaze into space. When work is unavoidable, I try to get through with it as rapidly as possible though doing a thorough job. If a little thought or planning will save steps or shorten working hours, I am an enthusiastic promoter of such planning. Also, if modern machinery and appliances can save labor, then I hold no sentimentality for the "good old days" when everything was done the hard way.

In my neo-pioneer stage, when I was eager to meet every task with bare hands, I still did not overlook the possibility of later acquiring various gadgets that would help to satisfy my desire for leisure. At the start, I was prepared for every discomfort and outmoded practice that my farming venture on limited capital might ordain. But I had no intention of remaining in that slavish predicament if I could avoid it. My aim was to exchange such initial evils as quickly as possible for comfort and every up-to-date device that would reduce hand labor.

The charm of an old well head and its mossy bucket is not at all lost on me. But I see no reason for trying to make a merry pastime of toting innumerable pails of water, especially in winter. I can look affectionately on the kerosene lamp, ready to admit, if only to be agreeable, that its light is easier on the eyes than an electric bulb, though privately I question such nostalgic asseveration. I happen to have a strong liking for electric lamps strewn about wherever commodious chairs invite sitting and which instantaneously shed lots of illumination. Give me light without any bothers—and no messing with kerosene cans, wicks that need trimming, smoked chimneys that need polishing. At one time I regarded the good old kitchen range, with its steady warmth and purring tea-kettle, as an essential bit of poetry in farm life. I used one when I first arrived at High Meadows and city friends unanimously waxed eloquent over its "hominess." They, patently, did not lug buckets of coal from the cellar or armfuls of wood from a snowbank to stoke its voracious maw; they didn't have to dispose of the amazing quantity of ashes it produced or cope with the dust that rose in clouds when ashes were removed. Nor did they appreciate that the stove's heat graph was as erratic as a Dow Jones average in a tumultuous week. I have since sacrificed that embodiment of hominess for bottled gas and a compact, small range that cooks an entire meal on the urging of just one match.

As for the outdoor privy, experience during two wars with latrines convinced me of the folly of laying bare any part of my anatomy in bitter cold weather if it could possibly be avoided. It has been avoided, by a fully equipped bathroom.

Such an unromantic attitude toward the quaint charm of old-fashioned farm life is, I know, rank heresy. I can hear the moans of those who have taken abandoned farm-houses, restored them to their colonial glory, and reveled in their picturesque achievement. But my ear is deaf. Now I know the price of quaintness. And though once I was delighted to sip a drink before a blazing fire in a big old fireplace, I now tend to shiver at the thought of the chilly draft caused by the same fireplace when the logs have burned out. My own fireplace may lack historic charm, but I know its modern steel shell diverts heat scientifically into the room and that a solid damper closes the big chimney when it is not in use.

Heresy or no, present-day contrivances do, beyond contradiction, offer more comfort and less work. And I suspect our forefathers wouldn't have hesitated a moment to exchange the old for the new. In any event, they contribute notably toward realization of what I call "horizontal farming."

"Horizontal farming," to me, means gaining a livelihood from the land with a maximum of time allotted to lying down, reading a book, listening to long-playing records, or just reflecting on all the work I would be doing if the calendar were turned back a hundred years. Farming can bring endless drudgery. It does, today, in every rural region in the United States. Yet in those same regions, more intelligent farmers are increasingly successful in eliminating drudgery by taking advantage of the remarkable progress made in this country in the development of mechanical workers.

Dairying, I now believe, is the best of all types of farming as a basic start toward this end. Machinery is available today to transform completely the dairying job of twenty years ago. The milking machine, of course, heads the list. Also high on the list are the side delivery rake, the hay loader, the manure spreader—all well worth their initial cost. Mechanical cleaners now remove all manure from the drops in the barn and fill the spreader parked outside the door. That device, however, still represents a sizable investment.

Cows themselves, I am convinced, are in close sympathy with the idea of horizontal farming. They spend a good share of their days and nights in drowsy repose;

and when they browse—granted that they have good pasture—they move indolently about, lazily busy at the job of consuming quantities of grass or hay. Then their internal machinery takes over, the miracle occurs, and green growth or dry hay is turned into good milk, yellow-tinted by the butterfat it contains. Feed a good cow, keep her clean, and she is a walking milk factory.

I have a matronly bovine named Maggie who, I know, understands my desire for relaxation. She has found an old rope swing in an abandoned orchard. Stretching herself out close to the rope loop, which is a foot or so from the ground, she sticks her head through the loop, rests it on the rope and closes her eyes in absolute rapture. Not one muscle need be exerted to disturb her rest, not even to hold up her head. A cow after my own heart.

Gradually I am making progress toward my goal, aided and abetted by my two-toed ungulates. More and longer intervals are becoming available for assuming the horizontal position, with conscience clear and nobody to say me nay. Horizontal farming isn't exactly orthodox. I'll never get rich at it. But how I like it!

CHAPTER 4

DAIRYING CAME TO ME VERY MUCH LIKE AN infant abandoned on my doorstep. I felt obliged to take it in. When I bought a farm, *the* farm, I also became owner of nine milking cows—eight Holsteins and one Guernsey. They had been the nucleus of a sound farming enterprise and were no more to be separated from the operating ensemble because of a sale than were the barn and sheds, or the house itself. The farm had been a complete unit, and it was apparently taken for granted that the new owner would wish to maintain it as such.

At no time during the years I had been drawing closer and closer to the big decision had I given a single thought to dairying. It had simply never occurred to me. When I chanced upon Department of Agriculture bulletins on dairying, I pushed them aside like so much blank paper. Cows just didn't register with me; they rang no bell nor roused the faintest hint of a livelihood. They were as removed from the scope of my planning as the raising of goldfish or the growing of Christmas trees. I never got so far as to consider dairying unfeasible. It just didn't exist for me.

This curious blind spot seems to be generally prevalent among urban dwellers who turn to the land. They, as I did, give thought to every other possibility of gaining a living from the soil. Goats, mink, rabbits, squabs, chickens, ducks, geese, guineas, on down to earthworms, the list is very nearly endless. But never a mention of cows. Pamphlets entitled "Dairying for Beginners" are available, but the city person is never counted among the beginners. Except for Louis Bromfield's exciting volumes about Malabar Farm I have yet to find a book that displays the slightest enthusiasm on the subject. Textbooks can be had in quantity but, though informative, they are so dull that after a few pages they are closed forever and cows are cloaked in still greater dullness, than which there is no more gross misapprehension.

In any event, I suddenly and unexpectedly owned nine cows. Where I had included one or two vague bossies in my subsistence-farming project, I was overwhelmed by nine. My immediate reaction was to sell seven of them, thus reducing the cost of the farm by a substantial sum and leaving me free to delve into the woes and rewards of subsistence farming. Pondering my dilemma, however, I realized my farm was in the dairying region of northeastern Pennsylvania and that all my neighbors would be dairymen. Obviously my subsistence scheme would appear a bit odd to them. So I inquired into the dairying business.

I learned that my newly acquired barn was equipped

with stanchions for twenty-eight cows—a figure quite
beyond my grasp—drinking cups and water supplied by
a pump and pressure tank in the house cellar, a motor
and pump for the vacuum line that operated the milking
machine. Then I discovered that the usual practice in
dairy country is to have a milk truck call every morning
and transport the result of night and morning milking
to a creamery for pasteurizing and distribution. This
appealed to me, for it spared me the task of peddling my
product. Finally I was informed that the company to
which I would ship my milk returned a fortnightly
check in payment for the total poundage.

Here was the intriguing factor for me, the pivotal
point about which I began to revolve at accelerating
speed. The great and disturbing uncertainty in every
branch of farming I had investigated had been that of
income, ready cash, not in great amounts but sufficient
to pay bills with reasonable regularity, a financial return
that could be relied on within limits. It was once a year
with crop farming, seasonally spasmodic with subsistence
farming, unpredictable with other livestock—which also
would necessitate building up a dependable market. Milk
alone appeared to offer the solution, for, though eggs
bring in a periodic return, I had long since abandoned
any intention of getting involved with chickens and eggs.

My questioning became more pointed. I wanted to
know how much milk a cow produced, how much feed
cost to make that amount of milk, how much the dairyman received for his milk. Assembling my answers and
striking a fair average, I found that a good cow should
make at least 8,000 pounds of milk during a ten-month
lactation period; that feed and other expenses accounted

for approximately half the money return on milk sold; and that, at that time, in the winter of 1947-48, milk was worth something over five dollars a hundredweight. Eighty hundredweight of milk at five dollars a hundredweight came indubitably to $400.00. Half that was $200.00. From one cow annually. Which, beyond all mathematical contradiction, gave a total of $1800.00 as yearly cash income from the nine cows I had come inadvertently to possess.

This was an extravagant sum, smacking of Croesus. I had spun some fancy dreams about living off the land, but never had I dared lose myself in such a financial fantasy as this. At one stage, when I looked to chickens and eggs as a source of income, I had figured that with plenty of luck I might achieve a net income of $1,000 from 1500 to 2000 laying pullets during one year. With subsistence farming, the monetary peak dwindled to $600 maximum, and there were plenty of reasons for cutting this in half. But $1800.00! One hundred and fifty dollars a month; thirty-five dollars weekly! I knew many people in New York who earned little more than that, and many others who earned less. Yet, with what facts I had, I could not find any serious flaw in my accounting.

There were errors therein, of course, as I learned later. Nevertheless, after these were included in the reckoning, they did not alter the result too drastically.

Eighteen hundred dollars a year may not impress the city person. And in the city it certainly means skimpy living with little left for diversion. But there is a vast difference between a city dollar and a farm dollar. The latter stretches much farther. Rent is a major item that goes into the discard, once the farm is bought, and here is a tremendous advantage over the vast majority of city folk and suburbanites who are obliged to disgorge a sizable portion of their income to landlords. Clothes are another important factor. Patches are no offense to social standing in the country. Aside from their practicality, they bear witness to thriftiness. There is even an esthetic note to the varied shades of blue comprising a well-patched pair of dungarees. I feel no sense of shame or embarrassment in citing my wardrobe, other than plain work clothes and shoes, as consisting of one old blue suit, which I expect to be buried in, and a few white shirts, plus a pair of city shoes. To me, it is both fitting and proper to discuss business with my bank president or the lawyer, clad in everyday working clothes, even with a few flecks of manure visible on my shoes. It is good just to be natural.

The food problem obviously is simplified on a farm, especially with a herd of cows. Milk, cream, butter and cheese are available in quantity and at little cost. The winter's supply of pork, ham and bacon is provided by a pig or two, raised and fattened for that one purpose; likewise veal, eggs, an occasional chicken, or a duck, or a rabbit; vegetables from the garden, fruit from the orchard, berries for the picking in the woods. Hickory nuts and butternuts can be garnered in the fall for cakes and cookies. And all this free or at negligible cost.

Now return to that thirty-five dollars per week and note how much more impressive it is. A good share of it can be allotted to food and still leave some fifteen dollars weekly—or nearly $800—to cover annual budget items such as clothes, taxes, insurance, and occasional new equipment and repairs. But it is a real problem to spend that much each week on staples and whatever additional meat is desired to vary the menu, even if one includes the best sirloin steak to serve five or six persons when company comes. Luxury products and out-of-season delicacies, of course, would boost the figure to almost any sum, but the country store doesn't deal in such fancy provender and temptation is absent. An overpowering craving for avocados can only be satisfied by persuading a friend to bring a few from the city—very firm ones, so that they can ripen properly to the exact degree of smooth, unbruised flesh. Food expenditures vary with the size of the family to feed, but two grown persons certainly can fare nicely on fifteen dollars weekly. A well-managed, economical family with three or four children can eat plentifully on twenty dollars.

However, some revision must be made of my original estimate of net return per cow. Experience has disclosed several unsuspected leaks in my financial milk pail. For instance, I had taken a price for milk to the producer when it was close to its peak, which always occurs in midwinter. Four dollars per hundredweight would be closer to a yearly average than five dollars. Veterinary fees and breeding fees likewise must be included. And, inevitably, other unforeseen expenses arise and should be allowed for. In addition, two or three years will probably be required to assemble a herd of tested cows that can be depended on to produce a minimum average of 8,000 pounds of milk annually.

Even so, the result is not to be sneered at unless you are afflicted with hopes of getting rich quick on a farm.

Milk at four dollars a hundredweight would give an annual return per cow of $320. With twelve good cows

in the herd the total would be $3,840. Feed for the milk-
ing cows, the heifer calves that would be raised for replacements, and small stock would absorb approximately
half of this sum, or $1900, though experience will per-
mit reducing this share to about two-fifths of the total.
About half the calves born will be bulls and sold at
once, bringing a sum that just about covers breeding
fees. Veterinary costs and incidentals being allowed
for, the herd will still bring a net income of some $1,800,
and that is close to princely.

On the other hand, no illusions should be entertained
about doubling the herd and so doubling the income.
Twelve milking cows plus the young stock that must be
raised for replacements make up a herd of eighteen to
twenty head. That many animals can be managed by one
man without undue exertion. Fifteen cows mean more
work, or less leisure as I like to put it; eighteen cows
plus young stock will keep one hard at work a good
share of each day. It can be done—in fact, I know of
farmers who manage as many as twenty-five milkers, in
addition to young stock. They make good money, have
a bank account and investments in bonds. But they earn
every penny of it, and maybe shorten their lives.

By way of comparison, let's look at poultry farming.
If it is agreed that the cost of a dairy farm is very nearly
the same as that of a poultry farm, the investment in
livestock is of major importance. Twelve good grade
Holstein cows will cost $4,500 at 1951 prices. The aver-
age milking life of a cow, from first calving, is eight
years. Heifer calves from the best of these cows can be
raised as replacements at a cost of about $125.00 each, a
figure considerably less than the beef value of the cow

she replaces when that is necessary because of age, injured udder or other causes.

Authorities are agreed, on the other hand, that poultry farming can provide a livelihood only after the flock numbers 1,500 pullets or hens. Two thousand birds are usually recommended to assure a living. Whether the pullets are raised from day-old chicks or purchased when they are starting to lay, each bird will represent a cash outlay of about two dollars, or $4,000 for the larger flock. The egg-producing life of a pullet is eighteen months at the best. Big commercial plants allow for only twelve months when, because of forced feeding, the bird is burned out. Thus, to maintain the flock, at least 1,000 chickens must be raised each year as replacements. For the 2,000-bird flock, some 3,500 birds would have to be managed.

Startling figures of egg production per hen are given publicity every day. Reports of three hundred eggs per hen per year are not at all infrequent. But no one should expect such results from an entire flock, any more than one might envision a herd of cows averaging 30,000 pounds of milk a year. A conservative estimate would be a maximum of 150 eggs per hen per year. Allowing for breakage, the total would be about eleven dozen eggs. An average return of forty cents a dozen for eggs would be welcomed by many farmers, or $4.40 per bird.

Now consider that a laying pullet requires 100 pounds of high-protein feed annually and that this feed costs approximately $4.00 a hundredweight. This item can be reduced considerably by raising one's own grain and adding purchased protein supplements, but that means real labor when the flock consumes 100 tons yearly.

Caring for the flock, winter and summer, will be quite enough to keep one man on the move most of his working hours. Gathering the eggs is an exacting job. Far more tedious is the washing, grading and packing of nearly one hundred dozen eggs a day. Just try it. Or if your wife takes on the chore, be ready for ill temper or a nervous breakdown. As for the two or three dozen cracked, and so unsalable, eggs per day, you are pretty much obliged to eat them. You might try that, too, just for a week, before leaping into the egg business.

In brief, a net return of one dollar per bird per year would be exceptional, and that year would be exceptional for the amount of work demanded, inexorably. Actually, when loss from disease and other causes is taken into account, the flock of 2,000 birds could hardly return more than $1,500, with the sale of worn-out hens approximately covering the cost of replacements.

To my mind, the comparison is not worth making. The price of eggs is subject to far wider fluctuations than the price of milk. The work required by eighteen cows and calves is about half that exacted by 2,000 pullets. And the net return is larger. In addition cows are intelligent and affectionate, whereas chickens are stupid and so lacking in individuality that any one bird is completely indistinguishable in the flock.

As for broilers, fryers and capons, a man would do better to hazard his money in the gambling halls of Nevada. Suffice it to say that the biggest commercial growers, handling hundreds of thousands of birds and thoroughly acquainted with the marketing factor, are pleased with a profit of about ten cents a bird, after three months of raising and feeding. That would mean, at best, $200 from 2,000 broilers, and if you toiled like several Tantaluses to raise four flocks a year, you would still be only $800.00 to the good.

Everyone has his preferences in livestock, a sense of kinship with chickens, or rabbits, or goats, or any of the many others. Yet it will take a lot of proving to convince me that such animals are easier to get along with than cows. Provide a cow with good pasture and clean quarters, accustom her to gentle treatment, and she is completely tractable. She is intelligent and affectionate, hence she demands intelligence and affection. When she gets both, she becomes a pet and the inclination is strong to bring her into the living room along with the dog and the cat. Denied one or both, she gets her revenge, perhaps in the form of less milk, more often by way of an unexpected kick which for speed and power puts to shame Jack Dempsey's knockout jab.

I am beginning to believe that my cows, particularly the young ones I have raised from birth, don't know what it is to kick. Neighbors have commented on the way I move about when the cows are in stanchions, picking out burrs, brushing them, clipping them, treating cuts or gashes. But I find nothing remarkable in it. They know me, they have confidence in me and they are intelligent enough to realize that even if I make them wince when treating an injury, I am not intentionally hurting them. And when I take time, which I do often, to scratch their ears, rub their throats till they belch ecstatically, or slap their smooth flanks, they respond with arching backs, quivers of delight and a soulful gaze that they must know possesses a good trace of the comic.

If I walk across a meadow where they are browsing, they catch up and follow me, sedately or with tails high, not for an apple or a cob of corn, as with the horses, but merely for company, to walk together over the grass, jostling one another to get closer.

The cow is easy-going by nature. That characteristic is enhanced by good treatment. Therein is the only secret about dairying. Otherwise it is the simplest way imaginable to earn a living. The fundamentals of dairying are logical, the refinements are quickly comprehensible. Experience merely adds to the expertness with which the job is done. There is no need whatsoever to have grown up with cows or to spend years gaining a knowledge of handling them. The only starting qualifications are a willingness to work according to a fixed routine and a fondness for animals. On the latter score, if you like dogs and cats or any other domestic animal, then you are certain to like cows. Bossy herself will see to that. And to clinch the matter, she will provide your living.

CHAPTER 5

In October, 1947, however, my knowledge of farming was almost wholly theoretical, and I had to learn many necessary skills the hard way. There was, for instance, the problem of the milkstool. Glancing at it from time to time as it hung on a post in the barn, I had accepted it as a functional object as simple in purpose as in design. Given time, I might have come to suspect its evil propensities, and so grown wary, but an intimate acquaintance was thrust upon me the very evening my cows were presented to me. The outcome of that first contact between herd, herdsman, and milkstool failed miserably to evoke any roars of triumph. There was a sense of achievement when the evening ended, but it was pitched to a sober note.

When I bought the farm I knew that a new milkhouse would have to be built before my milk would be accepted under New York milkshed regulations. So my first real job after moving in and before bringing the cows from my neighbor's barn, was to dig the foundation trench, a veritable canyon as it came to appear, three feet deep and two feet wide, the depth to make sure of getting below the frost line. I was overweight and soft when I launched that first attack with pick and shovel. When the last shovelful was heaved out, however, I felt as though I had been in football training throughout an entire autumn. It was slogging, monotonous labor. I ached in every joint. When the pick struck a stone, which it did with diabolic regularity, the jar went through my body like an electric shock. My fingers became so rigidly bent from gripping the pick or shovel handle that I had to pry them open and limber them every morning before I could button my clothes. Eventually the trench was finished, the mason arrived, we poured concrete, laid cinderblocks, put on the roof, and smoothed the cement floor, and I was ready for my cows.

Ready is a slight exaggeration. I was glad to welcome them home, but that opening night revealed how skimpily I was prepared for them. For the first eventful milking my neighbor's son was to give me an intensive lesson in the art of manipulating a milking machine, something my farm books apparently had left to instinct.

He was due at six p.m. Waiting for him, I fed my cows, my very own cows, with tender care, the books having been much more explicit on this phase of dairying. At six-thirty I began to frown at my oft-consulted watch, and at seven o'clock I was definitely worried. When seven-thirty arrived I felt the weight of catastrophe settling over me. The cows had long since cleaned up their grain and silage and now moved restlessly in their stanchions. Some started to leak driblets of milk; others bellowed their displeasure, each one inspiring the others to greater vocal efforts. I had horrid visions of udders bursting from unrelieved pressure, of cows going berserk. My lovely cows, welcomed with such pride, swiftly were transformed into great, hulking brutes capable of wrecking the barn and me with it. Even the thought that my dilemma had far too many horns failed flatly to relieve my grimness.

Seated weakly on a milkstool, trying to avoid looking at that long array of switching tails, I realized it was up to me to milk those cows. And by hand, for I didn't know how to assemble the machine, much less operate it. Too jittery to sit still, I walked along the line of bossies. One after another gazed at me with accusing and menacing eyes—except the lone Guernsey, who placidly chewed her cud even when I patted her rump. I elected her my first victim.

According to the books it was a simple performance—head against flank, pail between knees, left knee in the crook of the cow's hind leg to prevent kicking, and the hands free for extracting milk. The latter feat, according to instructions, was accomplished by tightening thumb and forefinger about the teat just below the udder to close the canal and pressing with the other fingers successively to force out the milk. A succinct, easily understood explanation.

Somehow my hands weren't as free as the book said they would be. The three-legged milkstool demanded too much attention. As Bossy fidgeted away from me I was compelled to lean forward, tilting on one or two of the stool's legs. The outcome was always the same. The stool would slither swiftly from beneath me. When Bossy sidled toward me, I was pushed back relentlessly to a perilous angle with the stool indulging in the same perversity. It obviously found a morose pleasure in repeatedly dumping me or causing my arms to flay the air in an effort to maintain balance. With every shift of position, the stool and I parted company.

At last I rejected the psychological theory behind pressing one's head into Bossy's flank, which is that, as one pushes against her, she pushes back and stability results. Either I pushed too hard and she politely moved aside, or she pushed too hard and I, with only that devilish stool as anchor, was obliged to yield ground. After considerable coaxing I maneuvered her into place close against her neighbor cow, letting the two shove against each other while I got on with my chore. The stool was planted solidly on three feet in strategic position; once again I clamped the milk pail between my knees and, by miraculous coincidence, both hands were free.

I grasped two teats and applied pressure in orthodox style; grip as I might, all I could feel was milk flowing back into the udder—again and again, without a drop appearing in the pail. I began to breathe as though on the last sprint of a mile race. Sweat dripped onto my glasses, lending a vaporish character to my surroundings, my knees ached, my neck stiffened, my back caught a cramp. Still no milk, not one encouraging trickle. I shifted slightly to ease my many cramps, and at once the stool tilted and fairly leaped from under me.

From the floor I looked at my cow and found her eyes fixed on me, filled with bewilderment and reproach.

Those big eyes were too much for me. I unknotted myself, stood erect with due regard for half-paralyzed joints. Genuine panic came over me as I surveyed that endless row of bovine backs, each one representing a milking job. As for the milkstool, I kicked it with honest venom.

My neighbor arrived at that moment. I leaned feebly against the cow with a futile attempt at jauntiness, casually announcing I had started to milk by hand. He noted the pail, unblemished by a drop of milk, but said nothing. Instead, he showed me how to assemble the machine, hang the surcingle over the cow's back, swing the container on it beneath the cow and then attach the four inflation cups to the teats. Under his supervision, I managed the entire ritual, even to drawing a bit of milk by pulling down on the teat with thumb and forefinger, a manner of milking regarded by dairymen in the same unholy light as one-finger typing in a school for stenography.

With expert assistance I milked five cows in little more than an hour. The others were dry, a cheerful circumstance I had forgotten momentarily. After his departure, I was suffused with affection for those big animals, my cows. I dispensed hay with lavish hand. I patted them on rump and shoulder, scratched their ears, cooed over them, causing them to regard me with suspicious wonderment. I told myself I had been entrusted with a great responsibility. I vowed I would do my utmost to prove myself worthy. Such magnificent cows deserved everything I could give and do for them. I felt an overwhelming desire to lie down beside animals that returned so much for so little. My devotion was boundless.

The next morning, however, I spent nearly two hours getting my new friends milked and the warmth of my ardor was more closely akin to the thermometer outdoors, where the first cold of winter pierced through gloves and wool shirt.

Still there was Molly—and the dark mystery of harnessing her. My experience with horses had been extremely meager, occurring mainly in World War I. After driving an ambulance for a year at the French front, I was told when the American Army took over the service that because I had to wear glasses I would be useful only at base hospitals. With no desire to fight a war with a bedpan, I volunteered for the French Armies. In 1917-18 the French military wasted no time on such nonsense as physical handicaps. The one requirement was that you could hold and fire a gun, even if you used your crutch as a gun support. Physical examinations were taken in the nude state, but limps, bumps, weak eyes, deafness, bad teeth and similar shortcomings went without remark. If you could talk, hobble and move your arms, it was hard to miss a perfect score. I walked in wearing my glasses and was accepted with what might be called precipitous haste. I was ordered to the field artillery school at Fontainebleau and in those days artillery used horses, not motor power.

I rode at every opportunity; but as I was being trained as an officer, my horse always appeared ready to mount, and I learned nothing about putting on even a saddle, to say nothing of a full harness. Moreover, my schooling in horsemanship was curtailed when, during *manege*, or riding class, I got bored guiding a horse round and round at a slow pace and tried to improve my French by reading a newspaper. I made fine progress on page one, understanding no less than a score of words. Turning to page two, without thinking, I made the usual motion of throwing the paper open and folding it back. Only I didn't get it folded. The horse heard the newspaper crackle, glanced back, saw the fluttering white object and promptly took off at a pace far faster than anybody had suspected him capable of. I managed to hang on, though not in a manner to impress my instructor. On the contrary, he announced, in extremely sarcastic French, that I was more gifted as a circus rider and it would not be necessary for me to take to saddle again. Instead, I was to make sure the saddles and bridles were properly polished.

That was the sum of my knowledge of horseflesh until I became Molly's owner, though not yet master. To begin with, Molly missed a couple of pals she had been playing with in a neighbor's meadow. Whenever a gate was left open—it took me weeks to become really gate-conscious—she would spy it, amble unconcernedly toward it, then take off, tail high in scorn. Frequently a whole day was required to find her and coax her back. Leading her home required catching hold of the rope on her halter. But Molly was long familiar with that trick. She would allow me to get within a few steps of her, then prance out of the way. My only hope was to meet a farmer on the road and yell to him to halt Molly. With the rope caught, Molly would consent amiably to being led but with a derisive leer in her eye. She knew I would forget again to close a gate and the game would start anew.

I am not entirely innocent of procrastination. I am especially susceptible when something must be done that I don't understand. Knowing nothing about harnessing a horse, I put off from day to day an attempt to do so— even when delay forced me to do work every farmer expects of a horse.

There were two daily chores for a horse—hauling manure and delivering my milk to a neighbor's barn, since the milk-truck driver had decided not to call at my hilltop barn until spring. Until snow fell I ran the milk down in my car. A wheelbarrow was my solution for manure, pending a struggle to the finish with the harness.

The projected vegetable garden beyond the house from the barn was my initial manure target. Each morning I cast a withering gaze on the cows for producing so much dung in a mere twenty-four hours, then set to work. I wheeled eight heaping barrowfuls per day up and down slopes, over rough sod and ruts to the chosen expanse of tangled weeds. The vision, almost the taste on my tongue, of sweet corn, green peas, asparagus and all the rest of the seed-catalog list, kept me going.

Soon my manure mounds, mathematically spaced for later spreading, filled my garden plot. Potential flower beds around the house were my next goal, and I pictured majestic delphiniums, lordly hollyhocks, spicy phlox along with such intriguing blooms as salpiglossis, coreopsis and scabiosa. In two days the flower beds had enough manure to grow giant specimens of every selection. Next came the herb garden with the flavor of sweet basil in spaghetti sauce, thyme in lamb ragout, sage with baked spareribs, and sweet marjoram, summer savory and rosemary for soups as gastronomic spurs to my energies. Four barrowfuls, half the daily production, completely covered the herb garden.

Still lacking the courage to try to get Molly and her harness into a working unit, I planned a splendid little pasture for calves near the barn. But the vista of calves cavorting gaily about in their own meadow lacked the sustaining power of my other colorful visions. By the time half the area was dotted with manure heaps, I didn't give a damn how cute the gamboling calves would look. (Of course, I didn't know then that calves should not be turned into pasture until they are almost a year old.) Nevertheless, I plugged away, steadily reducing the distance from barn door to manure heap.

Instead of relief, I felt alarm. I was hemmed in, being pushed back relentlessly to the barn door by my own back-breaking labor. Once at the door I would be trapped, for no other manure target was accessible by wheelbarrow. I laid the mounds closer together, then next to each other, but the barn door was right at my back, yawning inexorably. So, blocked by dung on every side, I was compelled to turn to Molly.

The simple, direct answer to my predicament could have been obtained in five minutes if I had confessed my ignorance to my neighbor-mentor. I was absorbing a fund of information from him on dairying, and to have inserted a lesson or two on harnessing a horse would have gone almost unnoticed. Moreover, I had a strong suspicion that he realized I didn't know any more about horses than I did about cows. But I turned stubborn. Both shame and pride made me adamant. I had circumvented my ignorance of the dairy problem by stating that in the section of the Middle West, where, I inferred by vague allusions, I had gained some farming experience, dairying was non-existent. But I could not find any valid reason for asserting that horses had not been used, in a pre-tractor era. So, to save face, to convince my neighbor that I was not an utter tyro at farming, I wrestled in solitude with my problem.

Wrestled is the appropriate word for the contest that followed. Time after time I was thrown, literally, flat on my back or flat on my face. I would lay the harness on the stable floor, perch myself on a milkstool, and then by a process of logical elimination strive to get at the basic principle of the endless tangle of straps, buckles, snaps, rings and loops. I would hoist one section onto my shoulder to investigate other parts better, and almost immediately I would be floundering about like a fish in a net, getting deeper into my leather toils with every move. The spectacle ended invariably in the same way. I would trip, lose balance and collapse while the harness settled over me.

I studied mail-order catalogs with illustrations of lively steeds decked out in new harness. I prized calendars depicting horses at work and examined them carefully. On the road, in my car, I watched eagerly for horses. Spying a team ahead I would slow down, even stop while the horses passed. With what I hoped would be taken for a vacant stare I would inspect the harness parading by. I made little progress by this method until I concentrated on just one detail at each encounter. Thus I advanced from bridle to collar to hame straps to jockey yoke to yoke to breast strap to traces to breeching, terms culled from the replacement list in the catalogs.

By the time I reached the breeching for the horse's rear, and was feeling very much like one, I realized what should have been plain at the start—that the harness could be thrown over the equine back like a blanket and held in place by just two buckles, for the hames and the bellyband. This revelation kindled anew an enthusiasm that had been close to cold ashes.

For several hours Molly was obliged to stand in her stall while I practiced throwing the harness across her broad back so that it would fall approximately into place. But a work harness weighs a lot of pounds—about fifty, I believe—and is not suited to accurate casting. Various parts lasso stall posts, the horse's head and your own worthless neck. Molly survived her ordeal by rolling her eyes, switching her tail and chewing furiously at the rim of her manger as, by sheer strength, I dragged the hames along her back and to her collar.

The manger might have been reduced to splinters had chance not favored me. In hauling the mass of leather off Molly's rump I happened to get the breeching ring (that ought to be its name but it's not in my catalog) over my right shoulder, thus supporting the aft end of the harness and leaving my hands free to cope with the fore end. Holding that position, I tried to restrain my puffing and made a fresh attack. One hame went right over Molly's withers and landed close to the collar. The other hame dropped neatly into place. And with a shrug I shed the remainder of the harness across Molly's haunches. It was miraculous, like a photo-cell door, like a lovely flower opening upside down.

However, I had not solved the entire problem. Prior to my arrival on the farm, Molly had had a harness mate. Hence the wagon and all machinery were equipped for team hitching. Since I had no intention of coping with more than one horse that first winter, I realized I would have to manufacture a one-horse hitch, a bit of engineering that baffled me. Fortunately, two neighbors dropped in one Sunday morning; I made casual reference to the fact that I would have to rig up a one-horse hitch for Molly and, to my unexpressed delight, they went to work. A one-bob sled, with box, was hauled onto the stable floor, the pole for a team was removed, a pair of shafts was resurrected and held in place while the long bolt was shoved through and bolted. Sections of old tire chains were wired on to take some of the strain when turning and the contraption was shoved out the door, ready for work. My neighbors were late for their Sunday dinner, but they had performed a much appreciated Christian act on that December Sabbath.

Snow began to fall that same evening. The big flakes came down with weighty purposefulness. After milking I watched them as they plunged through the white arc cast by the yard light, noting how quickly the ground was being covered. Snow like that through the night would make it difficult, if not impossible, to haul milk with the car. I was most grateful for the sled waiting at the barn door, but I did not join whole-heartedly in the rollicking spirits of my wife and son, who had come out for the Christmas holidays, as they romped in the snow. Through the descending flakes I could see only the hazy outlines of a horse, a harness and a sled, all to be assembled into a working unit. In bed that night I spent wakeful hours rehearsing the sequence of moves required to get Molly into harness and hitched. Then it was five a.m. I dressed and washed, had my habitual glass of tea and went to the barn.

A good six inches of snow blanketed the lawn between house and barn, covered shed and barn roofs so that they vanished against the white background of the sloping meadows. Big flakes still fell in the luminous silence that was theatrical in its tenseness. But I had scant inclination for pleasure in theatrics.

Ordinarily I shake off the pressure that tends to mount as some activity rises to a climax. I can turn my thoughts into other channels where tension is hardly noticeable. On that morning, however, there was no possibility of keeping the pressure gauge much below the blowing-off point. By the time I was half through milking I was far warmer than the temperature warranted. In those early days milking commanded my full concentration, yet again and again I had to pull away forcibly from mental rehearsals of the harnessing job that waited remorselessly. I imagined a harness on each cow as I milked her and tried to fit shafts into it.

I knew by my watch that milking was proceeding at normal pace, yet the delay seemed interminable before an udder grew soft and gave forth its last driblet of milk. I caught myself arguing that it couldn't be done, that the strain wasn't worth the amount of milk I had to ship. I figured the cash value of the milk and vowed that ten times the sum would not soothe my agony. I concocted a variety of plausible excuses for failure to meet the truck. I even went so far as to see myself cracking under

75

the strain, the whole farm project collapsing. And I felt very sorry for myself.

Yet I continued milking, irritable and gasping for air. Finally the last pail of milk was dumped into the can, my watch said seven-twenty and I was due at my neighbor's barn at seven-thirty. Once more all those excuses welled up, pleading for acceptance. I could imagine nothing more satisfying than to sit on the milk stool and say to hell with it all. At the same time I was hauling the harness off its hooks. Molly, baring her teeth, reached for the manger rim as I puffed in beside her, laden with dangling leather. Soon the straps were tight, Molly took her bit almost graciously, and I led her to the sled.

She was quick to sense my nervousness. Instead of backing into the shafts she slid off at a tangent, champed at her bit, tossed her head. By standing squarely in front of her I managed to coax her between the shafts, hooked one trace, darted around and made the other fast, whereupon Molly gazed at me accusingly because I hadn't made myself clear as to what was wanted of her.

Suddenly I realized the shafts had not been passed through the rope nooses I had manufactured. I could easily have wept at the prospect of having to lure Molly between those shafts a second time. Instead I inched her forward just enough to force one shaft into its noose, and then after a struggle got the other one secure. When I backed Molly to hook on the traces, I was transfixed by the sight of shaft tips hovering about Molly's ears. There was nothing to do but untie the nooses and drop them several inches, with "Hurry, hurry, hurry" echoing through my head.

At this juncture, my numb fingers struggling with knots, sweat coursing down my face and pressure about to blow a valve, my wife called cheerily from the porch, "Can't you take me for a ride?"

I'll never know what miracle kept the safety-valve intact at that moment. For a while I just leaned against Molly's flank and mumbled, meaninglessly, idiotically. Then the nooses were lengthened, the shafts were dropped to a more decorous angle and a rope was passed under Molly's belly to hold them down. Ignoring my wife, I heaved milk cans into the sled and uncoiled the lines from Molly's collar. She promptly started to move. I made a wild leap for the sled, scrambled aboard and caught a fleeting glimpse of my miffed spouse while fully occupied with steering Molly into the lane and finding a foothold among the milk cans.

Then, in the merest fraction of time, serenity enveloped Molly and me. She was obliged to follow the brush-bordered lane, and I had only to stand up and hold the lines, though I was blowing like a porpoise. We turned into the road leading downhill. Molly broke into a slow trot. We moved smoothly, like a canoe on water. The only sound was the deadened beat of Molly's hoofs in the deep snow. Trees sped past, a rabbit hopped ahead of us before diving into the brambles. Cold, sparkling air flowed over me. Without warning, almost to my own surprise, I blared out an echoing "Wow!"

Pressure was off, the world was a most marvelous place and—the milk would be delivered after all.

CHAPTER 6

I HAD RELIED ON BOOKS FOR FARMING INFOR-
mation before coming to High Meadows because, after
ticking off the names of my friends and acquaintances,
I discovered I did not know one person with actual farming experience.

John "Tex" O'Reilly, of the New York *Herald Trib-
une*, almost qualified, though at best in a fringe fashion.
Over bowls of chili con carne and watered bourbon at
his manor in the Upper Black Eddy section of Bucks
County, he had bade me beware of a "hay-burner" on
my farm, a term which I eventually understood to mean
a long, tall, rangy horse that devours far more hay than
its work is worth.

"You want a chunky horse," said John of Texas,
where he had grown up with horses, "close-coupled,
solid, able to use his strength—not a four-legged barrel
that has to be crammed with hay and can't pull a pram."

I drank deeply at this Lone Star fountain of equine lore and have been greatly puzzled since as to why John's advice failed to make a more lasting impression on me than it did. For, six months later when I was compelled to buy, in a hurry and as cheaply as possible, a working mate for Molly, darned if I didn't acquire a horse that fitted every detail of John's description of a hay-burner. Doc is so long-legged he is obliged to use a kind of double-beat pacing gait to allow two feet time to get off the ground. He is just under six feet at the withers and he is longer than a couple of barrels. As for hay, he is more than a "burner." *Incinerator* is a better word to indicate his digestive capacity.

In late fall, when the only job for Molly and Doc is to haul manure—at most about twenty minutes of real effort per day—Doc spends the rest of the time avidly cropping grass, weeds, twigs, even straw if he can find it. When I go to the barn for evening milking I call him and Molly. Doc races for the barn door and his stall, well bedded with straw or refuse hay. He is so famished for the small measure of grain in his feedbox that I can hardly get his head up to put on his halter. After I finish milking I fork out the night's ration of hay for cows and horses. By this time most of Doc's bedding has been consumed. I stuff his manger with hay, and this is gone an hour later. By morning his stall is as clean of bedding as though it had been swept, and he is clamoring for more hay.

However, I get all the work that is needed out of Doc. And I like him—particularly when he hears my call, rears up his head and starts for the gate at a full gallop, mane streaming, tail arched high. At that moment he is handsome, a noble charger. Some day I'll play "The Ride of the Valkyries" as he sprints to the barn.

Since John O'Reilly's counsel on horses bore such strange fruit, perhaps it was for the best that other friends had no personal knowledge of farming to divulge to me. The outcome might have been appalling. Despite their admitted ignorance, however, they were curiously unanimous in trying to dissuade me from an agricultural venture. Theirs was a kind of instinctive antagonism to something unfamiliar. They argued from hearsay and third-hand yarns of certain failure for the city man. Yet they spoke pontifically, as though their pronouncements were beyond contradiction. For a time I wavered, dismayed by such a solid front of dark forebodings, but after I had been informed with grave finality that farmers "don't live, they barely exist," I began to cheer up. Everything else I had heard from them seemed as absurd as this sweeping generalization.

So I was compelled to turn to books for what I wanted to learn. Soon I was able to discourse with apparent authority on soil conservation, crop rotation, organic farming, composting. I could name most of the trace minerals that should be present in good soil; I could refer with impressive casualness to antibiotics, fungi, molds and enzymes. But on my porch one afternoon, absorbing the warm October sun, I awoke to the fact that I owned a herd of cows with 155 acres of fields, pasture and woods that had to provide most of the feed for the cows. That relationship between cows and land demanded a lot of organizing and it still does, antibiotics, or no.

"The lay of the land" was not new to me as an expression. I certainly had used it on numerous occasions. Yet I never had grasped its literal meaning. Now I understand how deep-felt a compliment is being paid when a farmer remarks, "Those fields lay good," and how much of a danger signal he is waving when he says, "That farm don't lay too good." With fine terseness he is saying that a certain piece of land is, or is not, well drained, easy to get to and from, easy to work; he is summing up the vast difference between the hard work which a farmer counts as reasonable and the back-breaking drudgery that usually returns skimpy dividends. But my books had imparted no hint of this secret, though it is primary to any farmer, especially an urbanite turning farmer.

When I bought High Meadows I was enchanted by what I might then have called "the lay of the land." It was an ideal setting, to my city eye, and it still is. Evening after evening I revel in it. Here is solitude—not the awesome solitude of the mountains or the aching silence of the desert, but a friendly, intimate solitude that lifts the spirit. For neighbor voices, muted but audible, can be heard calling the cows when the wind is in the right direction. Here is privacy in the open, a seclusion that would not be augmented one whit if the farm were the only one in the heart of a wilderness. I walk naked from the milkhouse to the house, after a sponge dowsing with cold spring water during which I can splash at will with only a concrete floor to get wet; and only visitors coming up my own lane can force me to dash for cover.

So I am deeply attached to my embracing hills, my green slopes and rolling meadows. Enjoying them from a comfortable chair on the porch, I find nothing I would alter. From there, the lay of the land is perfect. But enjoyment bogs down when a hay wagon or a mowing machine is substituted for the chair. Then "the lay of the land" takes on a new meaning.

East Meadow is fine. It lies almost flat and, though well above the level of the barn, it is not hard to get to. The horses think nothing of the slow, twisting climb to its gate, particularly with the empty hay wagon. And often during haying, when the day's final load is piling high, just as the sun sets and luminous dusk slips over the countryside, we pause—my wife, if she is along to drive the horses; Scoop and I, who are making the load—and sort of suck in, through eyes, nose, mouth, even pores, an ecstasy wholly new to us. This is serenity unrivalled. And if all my meadows were comparable, the sensation might become almost painful.

But South Meadow offers problems, not really serious ones but bothersome. One corner, which drops down to the barn, is almost too steep to work. The mowing machine rides at such an angle that it threatens to tip over if nudged ever so slightly by a hidden stone. Making a downhill turn with a loaded hay wagon is a constant gamble against capsizing, and many times we have clawed for a handhold as part of the load slithered from beneath us to the ground. Fortunately, the ride to the barn is downhill. This the horses appreciate, though it takes a bit of maneuvering to get them squared off properly, since the gate cannot be entered at an angle.

West Meadow is a form of punishment for all of us, horses included. The land falls away gradually on the upper half and is not too difficult to traverse even with a full load of hay. From there on, however, the pitch is sharper all the way to the boundary fence. A further handicap is that surplus water from the spring has channeled a course through the lower half, making a shallow gully bordered by miry ground that the horses don't like. Neither do I. Down in that pocket the horses begin to protest. Doc looks over his shoulder with resentment at the hay loader hooked on the wagon. It is a fairly heavy object itself, and when it is picking up a heavy windrow of hay its weight increases by a couple of square roots of something. When the load reaches a certain poundage, which Doc seems to recognize down to the ounce, he quits, ready to turn in his time card.

I have given up battling Doc when he reaches this stage. His stubbornness is supreme. Molly has a fighting spirit, and she will pull until she is wheezing like an old threshing engine and is utterly fagged. But not Doc. He belongs to an equine union with rigid regulations on labor. That first summer I tried wheedling him—without result. I tried leading him, speaking coaxing words. In exasperation, I finally tried a few solid whacks with a stick. That brought results, but not the kind I wanted. He started to back up, dragging Molly with him. The hay loader buckled off at a tangent and the wagon threatened to demolish it.

So I abandoned the stick and, in surrender, unhooked the hay loader and once again told Doc to giddap. Still suspicious, he gave an experimental tug at the traces. Satisfied that the load had been sufficiently reduced, he joined with Molly and zigzagged the wagon up the slope and into the barn . . . The procedure has not varied since. When Doc quits, we humbly submit to his decision,

83

unhook the loader and drive to the barn, even with only half a load of hay. We gain time in the end.

Doc's obstinacy, however, is not sheer perversity. One day, when the ground was dry and hard, we noticed that Doc slipped more than Molly if he was pulling hard. We realized then that his hoofs were softer, more brittle, than Molly's and, worn smooth by turf, could not get as good a foothold. I had heard that horses need not be shod except in winter, when caulks in the shoes permit them to travel over ice or hard snow, but all horses apparently are not the same. I bought shoes and a neighbor put them on both horses. The change in Doc was immediate. Feeling secure on his long legs, he relaxed his union rules noticeably, allowing the load to be increased by a couple of hundred pounds. Then, however, the regulations were again invoked. Doc would halt, with unmistakable finality, and gaze with fine disdain at the loader. Not until it was unfastened would he consent to strain a muscle.

The root of my problems with the horses was ignorance, of course, and lack of experience. I didn't know then and still am never too sure just how big a load a team should haul, how much of a slope two horses can be expected to climb with an average load, or, when they balk, whether they are plain lazy or being taxed beyond their strength. The upshot is a schizophrenic situation. Either I am too lenient, willing to accept the equine vote on what should be done; or, on occasion, when I am weary after a day of haying and want to get the last load to the barn, I find my temper starting to boil if the horses seem unwilling to do their share and I apply a switch or a stick with aggravated vigor. However, I have yet to emerge victor in such a contest. Doc has my number and has inveigled Molly into his plot. Invariably they start backing up and, to avoid an inextricable tangle of machinery or the demolishing of a stone wall, I give in.

So Doc and Molly and I get along reasonably well. I'll never be able to use that rural weapon of last resort —a whip made of two or three pieces of barbed wire fastened on a stick. Nor could I belabor Molly's nose with a club as—the scars still show—once was done when she balked. Perhaps the horses count on my lack of sternness. I often wonder if they tell each other I'm a softy, a push-over. Possibly farm horses should not be petted, shown too much kindness. I suppose an argument could be made on that score, based on the contention that work horses are too coarse-fibered, too insensitive, too brutish, to understand such treatment and reward it with other than increased laziness. But I shall continue to disagree.

Somebody else might get more work out of my team, but I wonder if he would be nuzzled gently by Molly and glimpse in her clear, direct eyes a compound of humor, contentment and complete lack of fear. And how long would it be before Doc would again fling his head aside at the slightest unexpected movement in front of him—a defensive gesture dating from his earlier days when a blow on the head was his customary lot? It took two years of patient effort to rid him of that memory so that now I can even smack him soundly, but affectionately, on the cheek and he merely grins. Or is it a yawn?

North Meadow presents a terrain similar to that of West Meadow, high at one end and dipping fast to the south into a triangular pocket between a road and a ravine, a devilish place to operate in. The field is divided by the ravine, through which a brook roars or trickles according to the time of year. A two-acre plot is level and easy to work. Half of the other seven acres provoke a lot of sweat and profanity. North Meadow, moreover, is a quarter-mile from the barn, across a woods pasture. But the drive itself is delightful. Tall hickories stand aloof in the open; two giant oaks dominate the wooded slope covered with black birch, beech, ash and hemlock. Wild berries abound, and during haying season a hatful of blackcaps or blackberries, gathered in a few moments, is a juicy reward for a dry and dusty throat.

One catches a glimpse of the enchanted garden on this trip. Some earlier inhabitant with a redoubtable zeal for muscle-tearing toil, must have chosen the spot blind-folded. As far as I can perceive there was no good rea-son whatsoever for selecting this site, in the midst of trees smothered by wild grapes and big outcroppings of rock, for an orchard. It is far from the house and the soil is no better than in other much more suitable places. But choose it he did and with a giant purposefulness set to work and laid a handsome stone wall, four feet high, two to three feet thick, around his favored plot of a scant quarter-acre. With an impressive flourish he crowned the wall with selected flat stones which lean at an angle against each other. Then this indefatigable prototype of Johnny Appleseed planted apple trees and, I suppose, gazed with overweening pride on his work. He certainly deserved that privilege.

Now, of course, most of the trees are dead, gray, twisted wraiths of one-time splendor. Brambles have crept through the gateway, deployed stealthily and now claim a big share of the turf. Squirrels have sown beech and hickories where only apples were supposed to grow. But the stone wall still incloses that square of cleared land, and at dawn or twilight it seems as if the little people must come forth and take over there. Broad toadstools are there in quantity to serve as tables or dance platforms; rich, dark-green moss provides luxurious couches, dead branches are ideal for acrobatics, and spiderwebs, dazzling with dew, can be swung on. I have counted elves, brownies, pixies, trolls that came up from caves beside the brook, but no leprechauns. There are no Irish in this locality.

Thus far, the meadows can be worked, though the cost in weariness and bad temper may at times seem prohibitive. They have been tilled, planted and harvested for generations and it is hardly for me now to declare otherwise. Hell's Acres, however, is another matter.

Hell's Acres lies beyond and above South Meadow. Once within its stone walls and surrounding trees, you find it a marvelous spot. An arresting panorama extends for miles to the north and west, though bordering trees shield it from the house and barn. Tranquillity derives from its remoteness. Deer find it especially to their liking; and in winter hardly a day passes that one or more of them do not step lightly across it in quest of dry sprigs of alfalfa or clover. The field "lays good" in its own right, but it certainly "lays bad" with relation to the barn.

I paid no attention to the field the first year except to leave it open as pasture for any cows energetic enough to climb up there. Then Arnold, my neighbor's son, averred it would grow good corn. Since I wanted to get alfalfa started, we agreed that he would plow the field, plant and harvest his corn, then plow and plant it to alfalfa the following spring for use of the four acres. It was a practical and labor-saving scheme for me.

Arnold is an enthusiast for mechanization. He scoffs at horses, worships a tractor. *Hydraulic lift, down haul, power take-off* occur as frequently in his farm vocabulary as *yoke, whiffletree* and *trace chain* did in his grandfather's. A good farmer these days is virtually compelled to turn to machinery—except me, though defining myself as a "real" farmer might be debatable. As long as I can grow all the hay and pasture I need by plowing eight to ten acres of land annually, I figure that a tractor would be idle so much of the time that it would be an unsound investment. Moreover, I can't talk to a tractor or pet it, which I can do with horses. And I like that.

On the other hand, a jeep would be the real solution for this problem, and as soon as I can afford one, with the necessary attachments and implements, I shall return to the bank for a financing arrangement. A jeep could handle almost all my work and in addition serve for hauling feed or milk in winter when the roads are covered with snow and ice. The four-wheel drive would virtually assure getting to and from my mountain peak in the worst conditions. A power take-off attachment would be useful for various jobs, particularly running a buzz saw for fireplace wood. With a hydraulic lift attached I could use a plow, a disk harrow and a mower, completing such work considerably faster than with the horses. And on certain slopes in the meadows, the jeep could haul a big load of hay much easier than Molly and Doc.

But I would keep my horses. They can pull the side delivery rake and the dump rake, and most of the hay loads. One of them is needed for cultivating the garden. And in winter they would haul manure over ice and deep snow where even a jeep or a tractor would find tough going. So Molly and Doc would be worth their keep in addition to their companionship.

In two or three years Molly will arrive at an advanced age when even her great spirit will no longer be able to urge old muscles to heavy effort and her teeth will be so worn down that she cannot eat properly. Then the noble old girl will be killed as quickly and painlessly as possible. Doc probably will meet with the same fate and at the same time, though he will still have years of work ahead. But Molly and Doc have been bosom pals since they have been together at High Meadows; Doc needs the kind of guidance and control Molly provides and without it he might well become a hay-burner and no more. In that case to sell him would almost be to condemn him to harsh treatment by some farmer lacking the patience to accept Doc as he is. That would leave a black thought in my mind. So, better that he go with Molly, ending his equine career pretty much in his heyday and with contentment unmarred. Then I might buy a pair of horses that had worked together and were well suited to each other.

The point here, however, is that Arnold rollicked to and from Hell's Acres, known at the beginning as "Upper Meadow," with such speed and ease on his tractor that I was sadly misled regarding the job when I took over. I forgot the horses' viewpoint.

Driving up was no great feat, even for my amateur

horsemanship. The horses were shod and slipped only occasionally on the damp rocks that formed part of the surface of the lane. Also, the wagon was empty for the ascent, with roller-bearing wheels and rubber tires easing the burden. The descent was another matter.

The lane runs straight for about one hundred and fifty yards, with a sharp pitch, then bends left at a full right angle. The slope is more gradual for another hundred yards, but half-buried rocks are perilously close to the twin ruts which weave their way like a meandering stream. After a second right-angle turn to the left the lane leads on downhill, through a gate whose posts must be respected; then, a twist to the right, a quick pull to the left and up the ramp to the hay mows. Stone walls or big trees border the lane all the way, so there can be no turning out. Nor can there be any stopping. As with a roller-coaster, once the wagon dips down at the field gate and begins to roll, there is just one destination—the barn ramp. Barring a smash-up, all choice is abandoned at the take-off. It has the finality of fate.

At first the horses strain back nobly against yoke and pole. But those damp rocks cause intermittent skids when the load joins with the free-rolling wagon in a cumulative effort that increases speed despite the horses' best efforts. Halfway down, the acceleration is all too evident. The horses show less determination as they are forced from dragging steps to a fast walk, to a slow trot. With a gallop as the next and certain stage in the progression, they tend to bow to the inevitable by breaking into a gallop immediately. My opposition vote, in the form of pulling on the lines with all my strength while yelling, "Whoa! Back! Whoa! Back!" gets no attention.

The two rumps rise and fall as Molly and Doc move stiff-legged at a quickening pace. Then they abandon all pretense at holding back and sweep into a fine, full-length gallop like circus horses in the fanfare parade.

What to do? Just one thing, one and only one—steer for your very life. Feet braced against the ladder of the hay rigging, lines taut, I hang on, trying to glimpse the snakelike ruts through a watery film produced by the gathering wind. Those ruts are the key to salvation and every nerve, muscle and mental process is concentrated achingly on the single target. It's a do-or-die sensation, though there is no time for fright. Profanity doesn't help, for it is distracting. Air is gulped down only when direly needed, for even that is distracting. Those ruts alone are vital—twin threads uniquely leading to safety as horses, wagon and hay rush on, reeling in the threads as they appear just ahead of the horses' outstretched noses.

The first sharp turn is negotiated and the load heels over like a sailing ship. A twitch on the lines is a fraction too late—or too early, the wheels leap out of the ruts, bang on a rock, and the entire load floats through quivering air. It comes back to earth with a bounce, then on to the second turn. Suddenly the ruts vanish in thick grass, and I feel momentarily blinded, as though my cap had fallen over my eyes. But the horses are swung a bit wide just in time, then hauled around to the left. They let loose with their final sprint—through the gate-posts, leaving strands of hay where passage was a trifle close, to the right at the bend while I duck below the branches of an ash tree, and then to the left.

This is the supreme moment, the climax of this apocalyptic ride. Momentum should be just enough to hurl the wagon up the ramp to the doorway, where the horses give one mighty heave, the overhanging hay brushes against the frame and the wagon rolls lightly, effortlessly, onto the floor and comes quietly to rest in the dark silence. My ears ring with the abrupt quiet and the still air. I am unable to move for a few seconds, feeling slack and soft. Tautness goes out of my mind as from my arms. And each time, at this pinnacle of triumph, I vow, "Never again."

Some day, if I were to continue that wild ride, a line would break, or a horse would stumble and fall, or I would miss a turn; and the resultant wreckage would demand a lot of sorting. So I have at last generously turned Hell's Acres over to the cows. They are happy to stroll up the lane, browse in the alfalfa and clover, then amble peacefully to the barn. They do the harvesting and bring it to the barn in well-filled udders. And once again I enjoy Hell's Acres, seated on a rock, smoking and gazing over the countryside, with no harrowing thoughts about getting another load of hay to the barn and with no concern over the fact that, as a scenic feature, Hell's Acres lays good but as a workable field it lays very bad.

My embracing hills and slopes are the source of another problem in winter.

About the first of each year I prepare for the annual return of the ice age. Now I know how prehistoric man felt when the glaciers crept almost imperceptibly, but inexorably, across his forests and plains. I experience it in miniature winter after winter, with the heartening certainty, however, that early spring will come to my aid and hammer away with raindrops and warming sun until abruptly the ice, in desperate fury, transforms itself into water to spread a kind of climactic woe. At this, it is extremely successful. For several days I battle floods about the barn, build dams, hack channels through ice and frozen ground, and throw up levees of manure to balk the turbulent waters eager to enter my barn door.

Winters in Susquehanna County, Commonwealth of Pennsylvania, are on the rugged side. Quite fittingly it has been labeled the Maine of Pennsylvania. Judging from hibernal correspondence with Waldo Peirce, several of whose gay and lusty paintings flatter my rustic walls, High Meadows maintains an edge of two or three degrees' superiority over his native Bangor and adopted Searsport, and Peirce is not one to lack hyperbolic invective when he reads zero or lower on his thermometer.

The envelopes of his letters frequently are enlivened by water color. When the sketch depicts Farmer Rehm with a calf on each knee, feeding them with a nippled bottle, the postman and others are greatly regaled. When he portrays Old Man Winter breaking down his door or Maine bears surrounding his domicile while he resorts to giant icicles as his only mode of defense, I feel that Pennsylvania bruins are equally ferocious and that High Meadows icicles are bigger—and, indeed, that the snow is deeper, the temperature lower and the north wind infinitely more bitter.

Along in December come the first snows. Brown fields turn gleaming white, stone walls vanish, trees become intensely black. The landscape is thrilling; walks over the fields and through the woods are high adventure. By Christmas time my cluster of buildings is held in a shimmering white bowl. Branches of hemlock, pine cones and bittersweet berries provide a festive atmosphere. And everyone is in raptures over the beautiful snow. Except me. My rapture is diluted by the prospect ahead.

The snow piles higher and higher until a thaw arrives, usually early in January. Much of the snow melts, flows along the frozen ground to a flat spot where it backs up, and then spreads out, seeking a new channel. That flat spot is right around my barn. All the water from the south ridge, the east ridge, and the acres of open land and rock-strewn pastures heads directly for the barn, funneled over the meadows by the lay of the land, channeled by the walled lane leading to Hell's Acres and East Meadow.

The thaw ends after a day or two and the water freezes, in a flat sheet at the north end of the barn, on a very slight angle at the south end. From now on, every thaw, major or minor, loosens more water from the slopes and sends it toward the barn. But there it meets the ice and soon congeals. The ice piles up until the horses have to duck their heads when entering the north door. When they emerge at the south end and turn down through the barnyard, they skid despite their caulks and the wagon plays crack-the-whip behind them.

My first winter at High Meadows, the really rugged winter of 1947-48, provided an intensive course in ice problems. I now manage to keep roller doors from freezing solidly shut overnight. I can keep manure, coal ashes or sawdust strewn over a portion of the barnyard so that the cows can, as a rule, have their daily outdoors stretch without slipping and breaking a leg. But absolutely nothing can be done to thwart the insidious movement of my diminutive glacier. It creeps along the whole eighty-foot eastern side of the barn, gradually engulfs the north and south ends, then crawls off into West Meadow.

I was fascinated, even hypnotized, by ice that first winter. The milkhouse, located to one side of the north door of the barn, was my observation post. There was a drain in the milkhouse, but running water had not been piped in, nor was there a water heater.

I paid little attention to the ice outside till it reached the level of the door sill. When the door refused to close I examined the sill and found over the wood a film of gray, of the consistency of ice cream. It inched down the sill inside and reached the floor, moving just enough to be perceptible. There it spread out, heading for the drain in the center. Trying a broom, I discovered it could be swept along the floor and so found nothing ominous in it.

The following morning, however, I almost broke my neck when I stepped into the milkhouse and found the floor covered like a skating rink. I chopped enough away with an axe so that I could move about safely and later in the day returned to figure out a new attack. I discovered a new gray film slipping over the ice coat already formed. I traced it through the door and up the slope to the east side of the barn. There was the sheet of ice, familiar long since from slipping on it. During the day the surface would melt just enough to start the slow, lava-like flow of congealed water toward the milkhouse. The movement continued till night when it froze.

The next day, or the second or third, temperature would rise enough to set it in motion again.

I cut a deep channel in the ice, intending to dissuade the flow from its fixed purpose of invading the milk-house. Relieved when the viscous mass turned into its new course, I thought I had solved the problem. But the next morning the channel was filled and frozen solid, with the overflow adding to the ice in the milkhouse. By that time I had begun to worry. The only solution seemed to be to stay up every night and chop ice to keep the channel open, but that was obviously impossible.

Well, the drain filled and froze. Congealed water continued to creep in by day, freeze hard by night. It was two inches deep by my first sounding, then four inches. It surrounded the milk cooler, and continued to mount. When it reached the level of the doorsill, it backed up outside until the new level there permitted it to creep once more into the milkhouse. On my last sounding it stood an even ten inches deep, and my head was knocking against the ceiling after I had bowed it to get in the door.

At that moment I gave up. Worry was no use; there was nothing I could do. So I waited for a real thaw, a lasting one that would send all ice into a fiery limbo. Eventually warm days arrived, then a warm night or two. The ice went out in a rush, the barn flooded, and I had a hell of a time while high water lasted. But water was better than that diabolical ice. I could bail out the barn, which was more than I could do with the milk-house.

The moment frost was out of the ground I had a plumber tap the waterpipe from house to barn and run it into the milkhouse, where I installed a sink and an electric water heater. The ice still gets into the milkhouse every winter, but a pail of hot water flushes it off the floor and keeps the drain open.

In late March or early April the all-out thaw arrives. A south wind and clear sun combine in a devastating assault on ice and snow, on the earth itself. The rags and tatters of winter are shredded to the vanishing point; the soil loses its cast-iron cover, opens its pores and once again drinks down quantities of surface water. High on the slopes, the remainder forms trickles which join forces as they descend; soon rivulets are discernible crossing the meadows, and a swelling murmur comes from the walled lane. There a young river is having growing pains, refuses to stay in mere ruts, and gathers sufficient volume to tug at the base of the stone walls, muttering irritably at their solidity. By the time it reaches the south end of the barn it is in full spate.

But no longer does it leap gaily into the barn. A broad dike of manure meets it above the door, bends it gently but determinedly away and sends it on its uproarious way toward West Meadow, where it slowly fans out and is sucked out of sight by unyielding sod. As for the milkhouse, I leave the door open and wave the rollicking flood to perdition, down the drain.

The bottom-land farm "lays well" in that the fields are mostly level, but floods from spring thaws or flash storms are a constant threat. The fields, moreover, are likely to stay wet later than better drained, sloping fields, a circumstance which makes for late plowing and planting. My neighbor in the valley below has fields that generally lie much better than mine. But I have established with a clock the fact that the sun reaches his house an hour and a half later and the ridge to his west cuts it off another hour and a half before it does mine. That means a loss of three hours of sunlight out of every day. Even the longest day of the year has only some fourteen hours between sunrise and sunset; the shortest has about ten hours. In other words, I have twenty to thirty per cent more sunshine than my neighbor. As I am one who certainly would have been a sun worshipper in another era, I count that advantage alone quite enough to offset a number of benefits owed to the better lay of his land.

Along with that extra sunshine, the altitude, about 1500 feet, also assures a breeze on the hottest summer evenings, a pleasant guarantee of comfort when one is ensconced on the flagstone terrace. That same altitude, let it be said, joined with the wonderful view to the northwest, likewise places the house at the full mercy of the northwest wind in winter; and that can be an arctic gale. But there you are. You can't have everything. So I cling to my sunshine, to my panorama, to my summer zephyrs and do my best to forget the unhappy features which go with the lay of the land.

Land, as soil, the fertile agent that produces crops, seems to me to offer fewer problems than finding a satisfactory combination of workable acres and esthetic values. As with cows, no mystic learning or highly technical skill is required to make the soil produce good yields of hay. Anyone with intelligence can do it with work and planning, bad weather being the one unpredictable factor. In fact, the farmer today who does not get good yields, barring weather, simply is not taking advantage of up-to-date information which the United States Department of Agriculture offers free in pamphlet form, or he is too lazy to apply the information if he has it.

Buying an abandoned farm obviously is hazardous. The price will be attractive, but the difference between the bargain rate and the cost of a going farm may be considerably less than the sum of money needed to bring the land back into production, apart from the labor and time involved. Not all "going" farms that are offered for sale, however, are necessarily good ones. Poor management frequently has depleted the soil to such a degree that it is incapable of returning a good harvest. Such soil can be restored to fertility, but the expense and time demanded may easily defeat the novice before returns start to come in. A good "going" farm, on the other hand, has an air of prosperity which even the urban eye can discern—not a show place or an exceptional farm that will cost a large sum, but one with an unostentatious orderliness indicating that living there is not a constant scrabble for the bare essentials. Corroborating, or contradictory, information can be obtained by inquiry in the locality.

If the land is reasonably productive, the rest is simple, particularly with dairying. Cows require a lot of forage, summer and winter. They give back a lot of manure containing a big share of the soil's productive elements which the forage had extracted for growth. Obviously, if this manure is returned to the land, productivity is maintained at approximately the same level.

If, in addition to manure, lime is used every four or five years to overcome an acid tendency in the soil; if phosphate, nitrogen and potash are spread on the soil and made available to growing plants, then fertility is not only maintained, it is increased. And if sufficient organic matter, in the form of livestock manure or "green" manure (a crop that is turned back to the soil without being harvested) is provided to give the soil tilth, to keep it loose and friable, then plants grow better than in hard-packed soil. Worms will do their part, fungi and molds will do theirs, acids in the urine and manure will do theirs. And the whole problem of soil fertility is as simple as that.

Work is the only other essential, for the cost of the commercial fertilizer needed is comparatively small. Yet the work itself is no giant's undertaking. Planning and the skill that is acquired after a couple of years can reduce the labor factor to such proportions that any average man in good health can cope with it.

Grass farming is a natural accompaniment to dairying. This means growing hay and pasture, nothing else. No grain crops, no crop rotation—though many a dairy farmer still insists on the old formula of corn, oats, two years of hay, then repeat. The grain harvested certainly helps to keep down bills for purchased feed for the cows. Corn silage is a valuable part of a milk-making diet. But these days feeds purchased from reliable mills are mixed according to fixed, scientific formulas. They contain proteins, vitamins, fats, minerals in proper proportions, such as no home mixture could possibly rival. Hence they produce more milk, almost to the extent of offsetting the extra cost.

When grass farming includes legume hay or mixed-legume hay, then the amount of feed purchased for the herd can be markedly reduced, even eliminated during the summer if the cows are on good legume pasture. The clovers, alfalfa and birdsfoot trefoil are rich in protein. Their percentage of total digestible nutrients is considerably higher than in the grasses such as timothy, brome, red top et al. Experiments have proved that grain feeds can be dropped completely, even in winter, provided top-quality legume hay is fed, plus silage; and although the amount of milk produced is not as large as when a grain mixture is included in the diet, the actual profit to the dairyman is greater on every hundredweight of milk.

A herd of eighteen to twenty animals, twelve milkers and young stock being raised, will consume thirty to fifty tons of hay during the winter, the amount varying with the quantity of silage fed. Twenty-five acres of good land planted to legumes or a legume-grass mixture should normally yield at least fifty tons of hay, including a second cutting. A portion of this acreage can be used for pasture after the first cutting of hay. Another ten to fifteen acres should be planted to legumes just for pasture, in addition to unimproved woods pasture to be used in pasture rotation or for young stock and dry cows.

The total of tillable acres thus figures at approximately forty. Once legumes such as ladino clover, alfalfa or birdsfoot trefoil are established, they will continue to yield hay and pasture for four to five years, longer if not pastured and the soil does not become too compacted. This means that a maximum of ten acres of land need be plowed and reseeded each year. The work demanded to fit and plant ten acres of land is far from excessive. Even the cost of having the job done by a farmer with the necessary machinery is not at all prohibitive. Yet this is the total of toil required to keep hay-and-pasture productivity at its peak.

Wherefore I have become a grass farmer. I haven't yet achieved a satisfactory legume planting on all of my thirty-three tillable acres. Alfalfa, for instance, has not been too successful, partly because this is not limestone soil in this region, as in New York State, but mainly because alfalfa requires slow curing in the field and the weather is too unstable hereabouts to assure three or four days in a row without rain. Rained-on alfalfa hay loses so many leaves and blossoms in handling that, when finally cured, its feed value is greatly reduced. Ladino clover, with a grass such as brome, orchard, or the much maligned timothy, makes excellent pasture, but after the first year is likely to be too short for hay.

I am now trying to establish stands of birdsfoot trefoil, almost equal to alfalfa as hay but less difficult to grow and cure, and quick to recover from pasturing. At present I am seeding birdsfoot trefoil with oats, cutting the oats in the milk stage for hay, and leaving the birdsfoot to carry on alone. So perhaps I won't be long now in reaching my goal of a legume planting in every meadow. Certainly the cows will appreciate the improvement in roughage though they have done remarkably well even on straight timothy hay, with extra grain.

Such is the "lay of the land" at High Meadows. If I give the impression that it not only "lays bad" but "lays plain awful," I am guilty of libel. In this hilly country it rates about "good average." Without a great show of favoritism I might go so far as to assert it "lays pretty good." I know farms that are a lot worse and some that are a lot better. And even the best have to contend with ice and occasional flood waters, in addition to individual problems, major or minor.

CHAPTER 7

ALL FARMS HAVE DRINKING WATER FROM one source or another, but quantity is the variable that must be investigated, even to the point of obtaining sworn affidavits as to the flow of water for every month of the year—with emphasis on July, August and September, the really dry months. Old farms once functioned with a dug well and, with a small number of livestock, managed to get through a dry spell. However, not many dug wells possess the volume of water required by a herd of as many as twenty cattle, which can amount to twenty-five gallons per head per day. And cows are always thirstier in the driest weather, when water is scarcest.

Nevertheless, there are successful dairy farms in this region, and certainly in other regions, which depend on dug wells. When they run dry—and they often do—the farmers are obliged to haul water from the nearest stream. That is hard work. A milk can holds ten gallons of water and, when full, weighs more than one hundred pounds. One can may not suffice to quench the thirst of a big cow for one of the two drinking periods she should have to maintain her milk production. The task of playing Gunga Din to a herd is literally staggering by the time the last can is lifted from wagon or truck and dumped.

Fortunately, from books I had read I had been strongly impressed with the importance of water on a farm and managed to keep the matter in the front of my mind, even when spellbound by the view at High Meadows. A spring was the source of the water supply, and I made sure by insistent questioning that it was reliable, that, in fact, it had never been known to run dry. Two really arid Augusts since then have upheld the assertion. The spring has at times been reduced to a slender trickle; but there is a reservoir in the springhouse that holds about two hundred gallons, the drinking trough holds nearly one hundred gallons, and the pressure tank in the house holds another fifty gallons—ample reserves to meet the daily needs of livestock and humans, provided that sufficient intervals are allowed for the spring to replenish the reservoirs. There is a dug well, now covered, close to the house with a good flow of water, but we have never had to use it.

Drilled wells are probably the best guarantee of a constant water supply. They are expensive to drill, the average cost in these parts being about one thousand dollars, and this sum is certain to be added to the price of a farm offered for sale. In the end, it is worth the added expense.

Some springs are happily located at a level above that of house and barn, in which case gravity brings the water through a pipe to the buildings, even to the drinking cups. When the spring is below house- and barn-level, a pumping system is required. If the difference in level is not too great and the water flow is of sufficient volume, a ram may be the economical solution. The ram is an ingenious mechanism that forces water to a higher level, using water pressure from the flow itself as the only driving power. Nevertheless, it must be watched closely; for it ceases to function if the water flow drops to less than a gallon a minute, if there is insufficient air in the air chamber, or if sand and animal matter accumulate. I suppose that, if a ram were already in use on a going dairy farm, it might be assumed that it could be relied upon, at least for the greater part of the time.

But this is an age when electricity is the best hired man on a farm, and I prefer to turn the pumping job over to electricity. The house at High Meadows was equipped with an electric pump and pressure tank when I bought the farm. Water was drawn through a pipe from the springhouse reservoir and pumped into a tank wherein air pressure increased as the tank filled, this pressure sufficing to force water to the first and second floors of the house and through another pipe to the barn. The only interruption in such a system, barring an actual breakdown of the pump or motor, is lack of electric power. However, in my experience thus far, protracted interruptions are extremely rare. On very few occasions have I been forced to turn out the stock and carry water to the house pending repairs to broken powerlines. And severe storms are not at all infrequent in Susquehanna County.

The water pump that had functioned in the house before I arrived was an antiquated contrivance worthy of admission to the Smithsonian Institution. The motor also was old and worn, given to intervals when dazzling blue sparks filled the air, a grinding noise was most ominous and the whole thing became too hot to touch. So I installed a new pump and motor for about one hundred dollars. Since then I have been free of water worries, except on one occasion when I suddenly realized the pump had been running steadily for some time. An inspection trip to the cellar showed the pressure-tank at twenty pounds with the pump diligently pumping but unable to increase the pressure above that mark and on to thirty-five pounds, at which point it would cut out automatically.

I bustled about and found all spigots in the kitchen and bathroom tightly closed. In the barn, not a drinking cup was overflowing, an occasional happening if the valve gets stuck. All appeared normal in the spring-house, where I defied the chilly autumn afternoon by peeling off my shirt and sticking almost my full arm into cold, cold water to reach the foot-valve on the end of the delivery pipe. By this process of elimination I was compelled to face the one probable cause that I was hopefully dodging—a leak in the underground pipe either from springhouse to house or from house to barn, with the latter more likely since the pipe from the springhouse is copper and of fairly recent installation, whereas the pipe from house to barn is galvanized iron and at least twenty-five years old.

I knew the fragile condition of that pipe from previous experience. When I had had it tapped to run a pipe into the new milkhouse the plumber had scratched his head with a rusty finger and said, "I c'n cut it all right, probably with my jackknife, but when I try to thread it for a T-joint, it may be like the missus's spider bread, all crumbly, sort of."

I peered closer at the corroded and pocked length of pipe I had laid bare with my shovel and was inclined to agree with him. I quivered nervously each time he tapped speculatively at the pipe with a heavy wrench. It was too easy to visualize a small geyser gushing forth as the iron wall collapsed. However, when he cut through it, he found it sounder than he had foreseen, and shortly water was flowing in the milkhouse.

A second time a leak did occur. I located it when a wet spot became evident on the barn floor near the horse stalls. A friend was staying with me at the time, John Craddock, of the New York *Times*. We took turns with a pickaxe to open a hole in the concrete floor at the center of the wet spot, then dug with our fingers to remove stones and dirt, so as to avoid striking the pipe with the pick and possibly breaking it in two. At last we reached the pipe, tunneled along it a few inches and—there was the leak, a lovely little jet of water, a miniature fountain that would have fitted splendidly in one of those reduced-scale gardens the Japanese make, where, in proportion to the diminutive pine trees, it would have been comparable to the main spout in the gardens at Versailles.

We were pleased with the success of our exploration, but befuddled as to what to do next to stop the leak. Ideas were contributed, discussed, then either abandoned or held in reserve. Finally we compounded several of them and went to work. We whittled a sliver of hard pine to a point that would fit the hole in the pipe and stop the flow when pressed in and held there. We dipped this minute object in roofing tar to preserve it. We cut it off short so that, once inserted in the hole, it would protrude outside only an eighth of an inch. While I held the plug in the hole, with a generous daub of tar over it, Craddock made a few turns with adhesive tape to hold it. Close inspection showed not a trace of water. So we took a long strip cut from an old inner tube and wrapped that around the plug, stretching it so that it was extremely tight against the pipe. The rubber strip was bound down with twine, then with several turns of baling wire. There was still no sign of a leak. We slapped on more tar for good measure and left the hole in the floor open so that we could inspect our labor for a couple of days. By that time, when water failed to appear, we felt warranted in filling the hole. And, to my continued astonishment, that bit of repair work has held for more than two years, though I still walk carefully around the spot for fear of loosening any one of the several parts that made up the whole job.

I had all this firm in memory when the pump started to act up. And I had no relish for another bout with that iron pipe, which I was sure was disintegrating bit by bit as every month passed. In fact, I had just about surrendered to the enemy, rust, admitting that another leak would necessitate digging up the whole pipe and laying a new one. Careful examination of the ground between house and barn and the barn floor itself, however, revealed only customary dryness.

Once again the plumber came to my mountain. A variety of checks and tests left him puzzled and silent. At last he heaved a sigh, as though his faith in things mechanical had been deeply shaken, and said:

"Guess it's the pump. Sumpin wrong there. Must be. Have to get a new turbine, I reckon."

That meant a delay of a few days during which I would have to switch on the pump at regular intervals, then switch it off, but I could only bow to his decision. A week later he returned, set to work and soon had one end of the pump laid bare. Suddenly he called me.

"You like them frogs, the Frenchies?" he asked.

I admitted I did.

"Well, they're y'r trouble."

"What do you mean?"

He chuckled. I didn't.

"Look at this." He held up a mangled, frazzled object that might have been a rag a puppy had been worrying for several days. I gazed at him blankly.

"That, mister, used to be a frog."

Then I understood his witticism. Frogs do hang out in the springhouse. I never objected; if anything, I had rather liked to see them or hear them plop into the reservoir as I approached. But one had been too brazen or too witless. Swimming close to the foot valve on the delivery pipe at the bottom of the reservoir, it had been sucked into the pipe as the pump pulled water to the house. After a long and probably swift journey, somewhat like those dark tunnels of love at amusement parks, the inadvertent traveler had come to a mercifully speedy end in the turbine blades. And, posthumously, he hampered the operation of the pump. That afternoon I again braved the chilly depths of the reservoir and, in the name of future frogs, fastened wire screening over the foot valve. Henceforth, I foresee little, if any, interference with the pump's functioning until time once again has its way over man's machines.

A stream through the dairy farm is not essential when a spring or a drilled well maintains an ample supply of water in the barn and watering trough, but it is most welcome. The ideal arrangement would be to have fresh water available in every pasture. Cows require lots of water to make lots of milk and, if it is constantly handy, they will drink freely, particularly in midsummer. On the other hand, cows are creatures of habit and are remarkably adaptable. I have one woods pasture with a brook which roars lustily in spring and whispers almost inaudibly in August, unless rainfall is heavy. Silent though it may be, water still remains in pools and pockets among the boulders and ledges that form the bed. It serves as a regular supply for the heifers and dry stock that I turn in there.

The milking cows, however, find their only water in the barn or at the watering trough beside the barn. The upshot is a twice-daily brawl around the drinking trough before they come into the barn to be milked, and there, with one drinking cup to two cows, the battle to be first continues. Heads bang together like rocks, two muzzles strive to get into the cup at the same time, and the resultant deadlock may last for several minutes while the two bovines glare at each other and stubbornly refuse to yield an inch. Soon each cow has had a few mighty quaffs and is willing to be more patient. But during the

hour or so they are in the barn, they take in unbeliev-
able quantities of water.

Apparently it is enough, for when a cow produces
fifty and sixty pounds of milk daily, as several of mine
do after freshening, they must be getting plenty of water.
It might be argued, I suppose, that milk would increase
if water were easily available in every pasture, and I
wouldn't deny it. Nevertheless, I would like to put my
cows to a test; I am almost certain the difference would
be very slight, now that the animals are fully accustomed
to drinking their fill twice a day. At the same time I
would never object to a sudden whim of Nature's that
would cause springs to gush forth in each of my big
meadows and my second woods pasture. That would
please me no end; also the cows.

CHAPTER 8

WHEN I FIRST CLIMBED THE HILL TO THE future High Meadows, my ideas about barns were somewhat disorganized. To me, a barn was essentially a cavernous structure, dark with inviting mystery, strong of ammonia in the stable, fragrant of hay in the mows. As a boy spending summers in the country, I had jumped from beams into mowed hay, watched swallows arc through the big doors and soar with uncanny precision to nests plastered to the rafters. I knew what a hay chute was because once, at a time beyond my memory, I had fallen down one while visiting a country relative and plumped smack into a horse's manger. The horse, reputedly a kicker when startled, was in its stall and, I've been told, snorted louder than I yowled. My mother dashed in beside the horse, so indifferent to its ability with a hoof that the animal stood stock-still and I was rescued.

113

Scoop called the barn at High Meadows a "noble piece of architecture." I agreed, being already wholly enamored of the farm. It measured thirty by eighty feet and was nearly forty feet high at the peak. Viewed from the house, the roofed ramp to the mows was on the left, somewhat like a great flying buttress. On the right stood the silo, uncapped, like a cathedral tower awaiting its spire. In my entranced state, I found a cathedral atmosphere inside the barn as well—in the umbrageous silence of the mows, in the sunlight struggling through dusty windows in the stable. I was convinced that destiny had been fulfilled because we own one of Arthur Dove's loveliest paintings, "The Red Silo," acquired years ago, and it bears a startling resemblance to this barn and ramp and silo.

At intervals, emerging from my trance, I tried to recall the more important points to bear in mind when inspecting a barn for defects. I walked around the big structure to examine the roof, and finding all the roofing paper neatly in place, I concluded that there would be no leaks. It never occurred to me to get into the mows on a sunny day and look for pinpoints of light in the roof—the sure way to discover leaks. I inspected the stone foundation for the bank side of the barn and was so impressed by the size of some of the stones, the obvious solidity of the thick walls, that I promptly scored "foundation" from the list. Some time later I noticed that one corner of the foundation is out of line, probably from frost and heaving, which forced that corner of the framework out of plumb—a flaw so evident that I wonder how I overlooked it. However, this trend from the perpendicular appears to have been halted by placing an eaves trough the entir[...] barn, thereby shunting off much of the [...] previously had soaked into the bank, where [...] have its way.

As for [...] cow barn, I confessed openly that I had no earlier experience to guide me. When I was shown stanchions for twenty-eight cows I could only nod in confirmation, for up to that moment the only stanchions I knew of were those on ships. I reacted somewhat more positively to the drinking cups, however—it seemed nice that cows could drink whenever they felt in the mood —and to the vacuum line, with motor pump, to run the milking machine. I could grasp the overall advantages of milking with a machine instead of by hand, for I recalled that the apparatus had been demonstrated at the New York World's Fair.

I looked approvingly on the smooth, concrete platform for the cows when they were in their stanchions. How was I to know that I should have measured the width of the platform and the distance between the stanchions? Cows were cows to me, as barns were barns. But that platform had been built at least twenty-five years ago; the stanchions had been installed at the same time. Holstein cows of that era were markedly smaller than they are today. Breeding and better management have added inches in length, girth and height to the modern Holstein, as well as many pounds. The result was that a big Holstein of today appeared on that platform like a modern car trying to fit into a garage built for a Model-T Ford.

I was totally unaware of this drawback at the time. And there were others I failed to recognize—doors hung on rollers that either bind or flap in the wind and let in quantities of icy air, loose windows, holes in the board walls stuffed with rags, partitions poorly fitted to the ceiling and walls and allowing cold drafts to stab at the cows. Such matters I had to learn about, usually the hard way.

The silo, a pleasing part of the barn ensemble, became a deep, dark circular hell to me, recollection of which still gives me claustrophobia in a pronounced form. I later sold it, on its foundation, to be pulled down and hauled away by the buyer. And when the last splinter had vanished I mounted the saucerlike foundation and proclaimed my lifelong liberation from such infernos.

When I bought the farm the silo contained enough good grass silage to feed my small herd bountifully throughout the winter. With enough hay in the barn also, I was immensely pleased with the prospect.

But my silo had no cap, or roof. The harder the wind blew, the more snow it sucked into its open well. Every afternoon I would open the door which was intended to turn back the frigid draft from the silage chute, but which fitted so badly that it merely concentrated the blast through numerous cracks and gave it a sharper edge. Next, at the bottom of the chute, where the silage was to be thrown down, I had to remove a bank of snow via a second aperture, facing north, through which poured an arctic fury. Then climbing the slippery wooden cleats leading to the silo opening and on up to the hay mows, I would wield another shovel, which I soon learned to leave there, to clear away the thick mantle of snow covering the silage itself. Once down to the brown, compact mass, I would struggle with an ensilage fork to free wads of the stuff and heave it down the chute, the idea being to provide a supply for both night and morning feedings or about 240 pounds for my eight cows. (I had already sold one of the original nine.)

I cursed the snow with oratorical fluency, but kept it sufficiently clear so that my cows didn't have to contemplate silage resembling a soda fountain concoction minus nuts and a maraschino cherry. Then the temperature dropped and came to like the nether readings so much that it stayed down, even ventured farther and farther. The silage froze, first around the rim of that black hole, then across the entire surface and deeper and deeper. The top several inches became rocklike. A pickaxe was the only weapon to attack it with. After a half-hour of hard work I would have enough of the top layer removed to permit use of the ensilage fork.

Good silo etiquette demands that ensilage be removed evenly across the whole surface, which thus remains level. My method was an open insult to etiquette. Once I got a hole started, I burrowed right on down, even opened side shafts—anything to get the damned stuff out as quickly as possible so I could escape from those smooth, unclimbable walls that echoed my every puff and almost deafened me when I yelled profanely. I piled chunks of frozen ensilage up around the walls until they fell into my latest excavation whereupon I would heave the slabs from another spot by hand and, after long labor, open a new mine. Not until the stuff avalanched from all sides would I dedicate an afternoon to forking the concrete-like pieces down the chute and out into the barnyard.

Soon I discovered that the ensilage thrown down for the following morning would have also assumed the consistency of cast iron by the time I came to fill my basket.

Up till then I had refused to feed frozen silage to the cows, though neighbors insisted the cows didn't mind and it would do no harm. Somehow, I couldn't bring myself to such an unsporting deed. Coals to Newcastle? This was ice to Iceland. Frozen food in a freezing barn just wasn't right. Yet, after several morning attempts to hack my way down to only half-congealed silage with fingers frostbitten and nosetip beyond sensation, I gave in to local custom. I dumped hunks of the ice-bound stuff before my cows; they struggled with it, licked and chewed it until it thawed, and seemed reasonably unconcerned. But I suffered by proxy the aches which I was convinced must have been theirs after such provender. My cows, after all, weren't a lot of huskies raised on frozen fish and blubber.

That long and wearisome siege destroyed permanently all fondness for my picturesque silo and all esteem for the ensilage it contained. I swore I would get rid of it at the earliest possible moment, before it should collapse or blow over from standing empty. And when I did, I was tremendously pleased with the decision. Now I jeer at silos every winter morning. My solution of the silage problem, moreover, has been unusually practical, for me.

When I asked the proper questions, I was informed that dried beet pulp was a substitute for silage and frequently used to eke out the diminishing supply in the silo toward early spring. I learned the price of dried beet pulp, figured how much my cows would need during a winter. Then I did some addition of costs, including the time and labor involved either to plant corn for corn silage or to cut young hay and grass for grass silage.

I computed the expense of hiring a tractor and a blower, which I did not own, plus two or three men for hauling the green material to the silo and helping with blowing it in and threshing it down. When the totals revealed that dried beet pulp would cost me about one hundred dollars a winter more than the renting and hiring, my own time not included, and I realized that I could dump a fixed amount of the pulp into a galvanized basket, add water, and serve it up and down the feed alley, I hooted again, and much louder, at silos. So I have been feeding beet pulp ever since. And I will never make a better investment of one hundred dollars for saving labor and time, preserving my mental stability, and freeing me from that black, echoing, claustrophobic hell.

Finally, to add to my sense of triumph, I have ascertained that the stuff adds enough to the daily milk yield to reduce by nearly half the one-hundred-dollar investment. In my more prejudiced moments I am likely to assert that it pays for itself, but I won't argue the matter. I'll call it quits at fifty dollars.

The silo, however, posed the only problem I could dispose of so handily. The others are still with me and, instead of bringing in cash as the silo did, they have necessitated a cash outgo. Nevertheless, they are being solved, one by one, and the expense they entail is a permanent investment. In the end the barn will be considerably enhanced in value. Or, from another angle, the cows will give more milk because of greater comfort.

When I inspected the walls of the cow barn with my best imitation of a knowing eye, I found no glaring defects. The windows lacked a number of panes—"lights" as I now call them in obeisance to local custom—and they rattled in their casings. I found a few cracks which required plugging. But the north wind was far more skilled than I at discovering cracks and crannies. And by the time it had begun to demonstrate its talents, cold weather had come to stay and it was too late to put up effective barriers.

I tried nailing long strips of heavy roofing paper to the lower outside walls. The wind, blowing merrily every day, took part without any bidding. Every time I managed to lean against the paper, using knees, elbows, head and hands to hold it in place, and then stealthily moved the hand holding the hammer, the wind snorted with glee and flapped the freed corner until the entire sheet slipped out of position. If by luck I had succeeded in driving a few nails at strategic spots and then reached for more nails, the wind put on additional pressure and promptly ripped the paper off the nails. I cut smaller strips, but they flapped more than the big ones. I found still narrower strips somewhat more manageable, but by that time the cold was so intense that my fingers were too numb to hold a nail. After trying to use gloves and either dropping most of the nails or bashing a chilled thumb, which is as close to inquisitional torture as I care to come, I gave up.

The wind won that round and continued to pile up other victories. If I closed a few holes, the wind merely concentrated on others I could not get at from inside and hissed at me in derision. I completely overlooked the one round I could have won.

There are five hay chutes in the barn for throwing down hay to the cows. I never thought to keep them plugged with hay. The only explanation is that I was so engaged with incoming cold drafts that the idea of warm air going out was beyond my grasp. Those gaping chutes were like five ventilators, up which what small store of warmth the cows exuded flowed unhampered into the mows and on to oblivion. Frequently, when I was pitching hay down one of the chutes—chilled to the marrow by the still, deep-freezer atmosphere—I would hang over the top of the chute to absorb the warmth that gushed up from the stable. Even so, it never occurred to me that such heat could be at least partly imprisoned down below. Months later a farmer made a remark that gave me a new understanding of the problem.

"It ain't so much the cold air comin' in," he said. "It's the warm air goin' out."

Since then my chutes are carefully stoppered every winter, and I look for openings even on the south side of the barn. The north wind may not come in there, but it can suck out a steady stream of warm air that should stay in with the cows.

The inevitable finally happened: the temperature fell to twenty below at night, and the water pipes supplying the drinking cups were frozen when I arrived in the barn, hurrying to shove my frosted hands between udder and flank of one of the cows. The water remaining in the cups was likewise solid ice. This was disaster of no mean proportions. No water in the barn meant turning the cows out at least twice a day to drink from the trough beside the springhouse. And I knew that ice already covered the surface of the trough, the water flowing off beneath it.

I finished milking as quickly as possible, though in those early days I could do little to increase the tempo, and lugged pails of hot water from house to barn. This melted the ice in the cups and thus freed the valves, which open when the cow presses its muzzle down and permit the water to flow. Moreover, water did flow, momentarily. When it stopped, I realized it had been merely the water remaining in the pipes. There was, I realized sadly, a frozen section between the row of cups and the shut-off valve beneath the floor. I set to work with a blowtorch.

It was like working in pitch dark. A good ten feet of pipe might be frozen, wholly or partly, or conceivably just for an inch or two. But there was no way to locate the critical spot. I started at an elbow joint, thinking that a likely place for ice to form. The joint got hot enough to melt ice but no water flowed. I moved along with the blowtorch inch by inch. I argued with myself as to whether it would be better to start at one end and work slowly to the other end or start in the middle and work both ways or, perhaps, gamble on a hit-or-miss system of applying the torch at various promising spots. Meanwhile I continued to keep flame on the pipe. And after two hours or so, water suddenly spurted in the cups. It was like finding a spring in the desert, like rainfall to parched sailors. And the cows drank noisily.

However, it was a losing battle. The mercury continued to drop. Day after day I sought the blowtorch and found the ice-bound section—until the temperature went to thirty-seven degrees below zero. I was pretty well inured to sub-zero weather by this time, but those several extra degrees were noticeable through gloves and many layers of woolen shirts and T-shirts. The barn, as usual, was like a refrigerator. I expected to find the watering cups frozen, and they were. But as I inspected them I noticed a small icicle hanging from the pipe over the stanchions. That was new. I looked closer. And there was what I had dreaded—a long, thin crack in the pipe between two joints. It was the same between the next two joints, and on down the line of cups. The whole length of pipe had frozen and burst.

I shall always count it miraculous that those cows survived that first winter. There were only eight of them in a barn big enough for twenty-eight stanchions. I discovered later that with every stanchion occupied there were occasions when temperature dropped below freezing in the barn—and that many cows, with normal body temperatures of 105 degrees, give off a lot of heat. But that first winter you couldn't see the cows for the stanchions.

Twice a day from mid-February till late March the cows had to be pushed out the door into knife-like winds and stumble through deep snow to the trough by the springhouse, where twice a day I chopped through newly formed ice to make an opening to the icy water. That hole finally became a foot deep, so deep that the horses were obliged to kneel to reach the water at the bottom of it. Perhaps the barn felt warm by comparison after those daily sorties. And the cows drank enough of the water to make milk.

More than once that winter I wondered if bad luck proposed to stick as close to me as Jurgen's shadow or if fate would accord me a day or two—three would be the most I would ask for—when the breaks would be in my favor. Each day brought a new crisis that had to be met and overcome immediately, sometimes requiring hours of time. And there was always a recurrence of old problems, easier to cope with because more familiar but still demanding precious time. There was never a moment for "horizontal farming." By night I was so exhausted I had to drive myself to prepare a hot meal though I was famished. In bed, still wearing half my clothes, yet temporarily chilly beneath a mass of blankets, I would vow there was little to be thankful for.

Actually, there were various entries on the good side of the ledger. There was plenty of feed—hay, silage and grain—and the cows stayed healthy. When I started to turn them out on warm days in April, they were in excellent condition, with good flesh, sleek coats and clear eyes. My respect for the ruggedness of cows, particularly Holsteins, was boundless. I stayed healthy as well, fitter than at any period I could recall. I left my car at the foot of my mountain and so could get to a store for fresh supplies, though I had to tote them on my back up to the house. By standing directly over the big—and only—register of the hot-air furnace in the house, I could get really warm all over, an advantage I often wished I could share with the cows. And I certainly gained a fund of experience, by bitter trial and error, perhaps, but imprinted ineradicably on my memory.

Looking back, however, I know that the outstanding item on the credit page was the schooling in dairying volunteered by my good neighbor Richard. Every morning Molly and I would arrive with improving precision at the platform beside his milkhouse. I would unload my unimpressive contribution of milk for the delectation of New York City, then rush into the barn—a warm barn, so warm my glasses would steam. I would take them off, peer about for Richard, finally locate him when he called a cheery "Good morning." (I remember vividly the first time he said, "Good morning, neighbor," for with that appelation I felt I was definitely an accepted part of the countryside.)

Then I would trail him about as he put things in order after milking, getting in front of him at every opportunity and firing questions at him with breathless speed. All my problems, all my woes were brought to Richard. Beyond shame, I laid my ignorance bare, asking only for guidance. And Richard, always good-natured, calm no matter how feverish my state, quick to show interest, never failed me. He had not just *an* answer, he had *the* answer for my every question. And he gave bountifully of all the dairying knowledge he had stored up in a lifetime of dairying. Moreover, he managed skillfully to make light of my endless crises to the precise degree that encouraged me without hinting that I was being laughed at. And I would return to my mare Molly and the cutter sleigh buoyed with new hope, girded for another day of battle.

Richard's wife, Bea, did her share by waving to me from the kitchen door as I passed, frequently stopping me to thrust into the sleigh a parcel which would contain a big chunk of wonderful cake, or cookies, or a slab of real pie. Bolstered by such neighborly warmth I would blow on frost-bitten fingers while Molly plodded up the hill and go over and over what Richard had told me, making note for the morrow of the questions I had forgotten to ask until, as though a stage curtain had been swiftly raised, Molly and I emerged from the shadowed valley into the bright sunshine on my mountain. At that moment yesterday's trials were left behind and, when we turned into our lane, nothing seemed impossible.

When suddenly April arrived, warm breezes replacing the northwest blast, I undertook my first job of plumbing and was thrilled to see water flowing once again in the drinking cups in the barn—a job I had postponed until the weather moderated because otherwise the pipes would have frozen again. Layer by layer I shed my winter garb. In the morning I leaned against the wall by the south door of the barn and watched my cows luxuriate in warming sunlight, stretching rapturously, shoving each other about in a revived spirit of play. In almost no time at all that endless, hellish winter lost its sharp outline, became blurred and stayed in my mind only as a brief interval to be laughed at. I even caught myself murmuring into my mirror as I shaved one morning, "Indomitable. Yes, sir. Indomitable"—a silly conceit which nevertheless was occasionally good for the *esprit*.

My dream barn was foremost in my plans that spring, for I was determined to spare my cows another such test of hardihood as the one they had just survived. At first I was intrigued by pen stabling, for even on hot June days I shivered at the recollection of my cows lying on a cold concrete platform where it was impossible to keep sufficient bedding of straw and sawdust under them. Every movement pushed another portion of bedding into the drops so that by morning the concrete was virtually bare.

Pen stabling means a barn without stanchions, where the cows can move about as they please, wander outdoors on moderate winter days, and feed at will on hay kept in movable racks. Deep straw on the floor assures a warm bed whenever they lie down. At milking time they are brought, two or three at a time, to the milking parlor, a separate room, placed in stanchions and fed grain while they are being milked. This struck me as a bovine heaven compared with my barn—until I realized that I was alone on my job of dairyman. Several problems immediately became mountainous.

First, a huge quantity of straw is required, for a new layer must be strewn about every day if the cows are to keep clean. This, by the way, is still one of the major objections of sanitation inspectors, who claim that cows in pen stables are dirtier than those kept in stanchions. I had no straw and, if I stuck to grass farming, I would not produce any. So straw would have to be bought, at as much as twenty dollars per ton. Bedding, even for a small herd, accumulates fast. The ceiling beams in my barn are about seven feet from the floor. One foot of bedding would have the horses banging their heads against the beams. And during the winter the accumulation might easily have a depth of two to three feet. The solution, of course, would be to clean the barn every month. Whereupon I pictured myself with two horses and a manure wagon, not a manure spreader, attacking a chore of that size. It would have required two to three days of steady labor. Cleaning a pen stable is really a job for a bulldozer, with two or three manure spreaders to move the mass to the fields. And big machinery was completely outside my scheme of operation.

Milking likewise would be a problem. Working alone, I would have to drive two or three cows into the milking parlor, put them in stanchions, feed them, milk them, drive them back, bring in two or three more, and so on and on. Such a routine would obviously demand considerably more time than my present arrangement—the cows in stanchions, all fed at the same time and milked where they stood.

So pen stabling soon went into the discard as a practical solution for a one-man dairy farm. Actually I never got sufficiently involved to figure what its construction costs would have been. Yet, all in all, my cows now are just about as comfortable, clean and healthy as they could be.

The old barn, still solid in its timbers and stone foundation though about seventy-five years old, has been sealed outside with roofing paper and sheathing boards. I have installed windows which fit snugly, yet can be opened when needed. Two-thirds of one platform has been widened, and the big cows now have ample room for lying down without their udders dangling over the edge and into the drops. Steel pipe set in concrete forms stall partitions between the cows. New stanchions, hung on swivels, provide amazing freedom of movement. I have watched my cows repeatedly to note how free they are to move about. Now I know they can reach comfortably for all the feed placed before them, that they can lie down and get up without the slightest difficulty, that a sudden itch on a hind foot can be reached and licked despite the stanchion. In such a situation a cow has no cause for being unhappy. And mine are not, a fact I am sure of just by looking at them and seeing how they get along. Actually, they are supremely contented.

Fourteen stanchions now form one side of the barn, with a four-foot stall for each animal. Four old stanchions remain on the other side, where young stock has plenty of room on the old, narrow platform. I have removed the remaining stanchions and in their place have built two calf pens, large enough for two or three calves each and with a drinking cup in between for communal use. At the end is the maternity ward, a calving pen, where the cows are placed just before they freshen and where both dam and daughter have space and comfort.

It is not an ideal barn, my "noble piece of architecture," yet it now deserves to be rated a good barn. I maintain, moreover, that it is a fair example of what can be done by renovating an old barn, granted it is sound enough to warrant repairs. I was obliged to negotiate an occasional loan from the bank to pay the bills for the renovation, but those debts were well worth while. In the end, at a cost of approximately $1,000, not including what labor I contributed, I own a barn which today would cost at the very least $10,000 to build.

Luckily, it is a "drive-through" barn. This means that there are big doors at each end, permitting a team or tractor with manure wagon to drive between the drops while the latter are being cleaned, and on out at the other end. The practicality of this is plain, especially in dairying, though far more than one dairy barn is not of this type and in such the work is correspondingly awkward.

The stable is also of "face-out" design. This means that the cows face out from the main alleyway, and the drops are therefore at the edge of the alleyway. Again loading the manure is facilitated, particularly with drops on each side. Nevertheless, some dairymen prefer the "face-in" design because two rows of cows can be fed more easily. This is a matter of personal choice. With a small herd, I find it quicker to load manure in one trip, instead of two, and carry feed to my long row of stanchions, then to the other side where young heifers are quartered.

At each end of the stable there is a storage loft. In one of these, formerly used for machinery, I intend to install two large feed bins, one for prepared dairy feed, the other for beet pulp. Each will have a chute into the old feed room below, allowing me to draw grain or pulp merely by opening a sliding door. Each bin will be built to hold about two tons. The other loft is used for bedding straw and has a chute to the main floor below. Between these lofts and beneath the ramp to the mows there is open space for hay; but as yet I have not needed it, since the fifty tons I can cram into the main mows are sufficient for my needs. There are four of these. The two end ones, over the lofts, are shallow; the two central ones, on each side of the ramp, drop to the stable ceiling. I find this arrangement excellent except for one disadvantage. With the silo gone, praise be, and its ladder leading to the mows, I am compelled to go outside the barn to the ramp and then into the mows. This is not an inviting trip in bad weather, but as yet I have not been able to locate a stairway that will fit both the stable and the mow arrangement. But that will come.

The ideal barn is a rarity. It simply will not be found on dairy farms within a modest-price bracket. But so much can be done at relatively small expense with an old, but solid barn of practical design that this problem is actually of less consequence than it first appears. Moreover, any barn has to be worked in for a winter and a summer before its merits and its handicaps can be appreciated.

CHAPTER 9

Mystery yarns and thrillers are sometimes preceded by brief descriptions of the participants therein. Shakespeare's plays lead off with dramatis personae. A theater program offers a cast of characters.

Well, a herd of cows offers little mystery but it can provide a variety of thrills, day after day, year in, year out. I don't recall that Shakespeare ever found the cow an inspiring subject for blank verse but certainly she can evoke a flow of cuss words not far removed from poetry. In a group of bovines there is, moreover, an endless assortment of comedy, melodrama, drama and tragedy to satisfy the most divergent tastes. As for characters, I find more difference in personality in a dozen cows than in any well selected group of humans of like number. "She's a character" has become a tattered but constantly repeated part of my descriptive vocabulary.

The urban visitor to dairy country is likely to rhapsodize over cows grazing or resting in a green pasture where a stream chortles and old willows whisper an endless tale. That is a typical country scene to the city person. For soothing frayed nerves, for inducing the kind of relaxation that heals as no nostrum can, the picture is without rival. But the passer-by views the cows collectively; they all look pretty much alike and, as they browse in ragged formation, they seem to act very much alike. The error in perception is a gross one. On closer acquaintanceship each one is discovered to be a surprisingly complex individual with reactions quite unlike those of her pals.

To show what I mean, let me introduce some of my cows.

Maggie deserves first call. A big, raw-boned Holstein, mostly white with a black face, she is the herd dowager by virtue of an uncertain age that is at least fifteen years. Her back is as straight as a carpenter's level and on many conformation points she scores high as a dairy type. When I first met her she reminded me of a tall, raw-boned Irish cook I once had, placid as a rule but set in her ways, preferring to do her job—and do it well—with the least possible interference. Therein, and to a certain extent in physical appearance, they struck me as similar. Later, "Maggie" proved to be a happy choice in names, inadvertently appropriate, as when Scoop scratched his initial in some fresh concrete in the barn and, to flaunt the fact that he was majoring in the classics, inscribed the Greek letter *sigma* Σ. Looking at this from another angle one day, I read it as M, or *mu*, eminently suitable to a cow barn. Thus Maggie, after presenting me with a calf and following with a prodigious quantity of milk, seventy pounds daily for a number of weeks, became quite deservedly Maggie the Magnificent.

Maggie takes no interest in her title of dowager. She disdains any show of authority, though at the same time she commands the respect of the entire herd. Frisky younger ones never think of trying to push her around or engage her in a game of "shove me and I'll shove you." On the other hand, if by chance she becomes involved in a high-spirited melee, she uses her elephantine weight and power to plow her way out like a big ship meeting giant waves head-on. She is somewhat aloof to the others, yet insists on being close to them and is miserable every spring when she attains enormous proportions prior to calving and I keep her in the maternity ward to avoid possible mishap. Then she looks at me accusingly, as though I were punishing her for something she had not done, and the disturbed look in her eyes fades only after extra sessions of ear-scratching and repeated verbal assurance that she has done no wrong.

Maggie has a big udder at all times; when she is giving flush milk, it is enormous. I used to have difficulty milking her out with the machine because there was so little space between teats and floor to place it. I'm sure she understood the problem and so co-operated to the best of her ability. For she stood patiently immobile while I fussed and fumed, shifting the machine to new angles in an endeavor to make milk flow from all four quarters. Eventually we found one position which provided just enough forward pull to get best results from the suction. In this position Maggie must stand stock-still for four to five minutes. This she does, and as the last drop of milk squeezes into the pail, she lifts one foot to notify me that the job is finished.

Maggie is a big eater but definitely a gourmet. She scorns mediocre hay, which the others will eat, though without great gusto. But good hay vanishes by great mouthfuls as though she wants to get it all down in a hurry so that she can stretch out, belch intermittently and chew her cud in peace. Because of her age, I give her a quart or so of molasses daily as a tonic. She loves it. From the moment I appear in the barn evenings until I arrive with the molasses pail she watches me. When she spies the pail—or perhaps smells it, since cows have an amazingly sensitive nose—Maggie ripples from tail to shoulder. Only after she has had the first taste by immersing her incredible length of tongue in the pail am I permitted to pour out her portion on the feed-alley floor. When her head comes up she drools molasses like a child in a jam jar. She has licked her concrete plate with such energy that the cement is worn away, leaving pebbles nearly half an inch high.

Her ration of beet pulp disappears before I can serve the other cows and return with grain. But she takes more time with the latter. This is the chef's specialty, a dish to be savored and relished to the fullest, until every vagrant crumb has been captured by that far-reaching and all-embracing tongue.

Since Maggie gave me two bull calves in succession, I was convinced on the basis of the law of averages that the third would be a heifer. I wanted a heifer out of Maggie, the highest producer in my barn. As her time drew near I hovered about her like an old hen. Her weight became so great that her pasterns sagged and she almost walked on her dew-claws. So, earlier than usual, I put her in the maternity ward, where she could move about more comfortably. Eventually a marked depression appeared at the tail base as the pelvic bones dropped and spread—the sign that birth was near at hand. I finished morning milking with one eye on Maggie, decided I would have time for breakfast before the big event. I was back in the barn a half-hour later, just as the calf emerged. I wiped mucus from the nostrils to assure breathing, but it didn't breathe. The eyes were open but lustreless. I slapped it on the chest to start the heart beating; I moved the forelegs for artificial respiration, after turning the animal on its back. Between the spread hind legs were the four tiny rosy teats that assured me it was a heifer. But it was dead.

I cried as I left the barn. Out in the open I cursed louder and more profanely than ever before in my life. I roared and ranted and just plain yelled my wrath. And felt very little relief. At last I returned to the barn to administer to Maggie, to bring her pails of warm water and fresh straw for bedding. And there was another calf, halfway out, Maggie laboring quietly and with no apparent surprise over the second ordeal. One look at the calf's eyes, however, prepared me for the worst. They were as lifeless as the first one's. I did everything I could when the calf was free, but it was useless. And again as I worked over it I saw the four diminutive teats marking a heifer. Twin heifers—out of Maggie, Maggie the Magnificent, and both dead.

That was a horrible morning. Except for one thing. As I tended Maggie, I swear that she wagged her head from side to side to condole with me and to tell me with

her eyes, just as plainly as if she had spoken, that she
had done her best to make up for the two bull calves
and that whatever had gone wrong was no fault of hers.
So I put my arms around Maggie's neck, assuring her
that I knew she had done her best and that she was the
grandest cow in the world. Finally we both felt a little
better.

Now, as I write, Maggie is swelling for the fourth
time. A heifer? Or a bull? The odds are even. But I
have a feeling it's a heifer. I'm sure that's what Mag is
trying to tell me when I feel the growing infant against
her side. She seems to be promising me a heifer. Anyway, I know she will do her best. And if it is a young
Maggie the Magnificent, then it will be a truly happy
day.

Bella, mainly black with a glistening coat, is a big,
solid Holstein about twelve years old. She and Maggie
are the last of the original herd I acquired with the farm
and which launched me on the milky waves of dairying.
She is best described, perhaps, as businesslike.

Bella has accepted the fact that she was put on this
earth to make milk and produce calves, as many of them
heifers as possible. At that business she is a success. She
is not a fountain of milk as Maggie is; but in her steady,
stolid fashion, she lets down 8,000 pounds of milk during
a ten months' lactation period and better than 300 pounds
of butterfat. Those are not startling figures; but in view
of her age—a cow is usually considered no longer worth
her keep at nine or ten years—I count it pretty good.
A hearty eater, she is quiet, almost nerveless. Given her
rightful share of feed and reasonably comfortable quarters, she takes care of the rest. Never any trouble, easy

to handle, she accepts affection without ever asking for it and, in a way, without knowing how to respond, as though she had never been petted and now is too old to get accustomed to it.

I am not drawn to Bella in the same manner that I am to others in the herd. I might as well scratch the post next to her as to scratch Bella's ear for the response I get. She restricts her responses to those attentions which contribute to the making of milk and calves: feed and comfort. Kindness is included among those attentions, for I am sure that rough, impatient handling would change her into a surly animal, but the greatest kindness is to let her alone. A herd of Bellas probably would not be very exciting, but plenty of dairymen would vastly prefer her to more colorful and obstreperous animals.

Gaby at present rates as the best all-round cow in the barn though some younger rivals are pressing hard for top honors. I place her a small notch above Maggie because of her youth. She is a four-year-old Holstein, all white except for a black patch on her rump and on her face.

I bought Gaby as a bred heifer, fifteen months old. As young as that, she showed what cattle judges call "flash" and the upward tilt to her horns, resembling an upswept hair-do, lent her a Parisian air that resulted in her name of Gaby. Gaby came into heat three months after I brought her to High Meadows and I had to have her bred again. I was disappointed at first, for I wanted a heifer freshening in April. Now I am glad Nature worked that way. Many dairymen breed their heifers at fifteen months, but I have decided to wait until eighteen months, allowing more time for growth at a period when growth is rapid and should be completely unhampered by such matters as pregnancy.

At any rate Gaby grew fast and now, after her second calf, is truly a handsome creature. Livestock dealers single her out at once and have offered me four hundred dollars cash for her, but it will be a lean day at High Meadows when I sell her. With her present milk production, an average of thirty-five pounds daily for ten months, she brings in a net annual profit of nearly three hundred dollars. And she is still not a mature cow.

Gaby is my conception of an ideal cow. In appearance and for dairy type she could take ribbons from many a purebred I have seen in the judging ring. She is not a heavy eater and has the economic factor in her favor that her feed costs less in proportion to the amount of milk returned. She milks out fast and evenly from all four quarters, never objects to the machine and displays no nervousness. Her health is excellent, with never a sign of a malady since I have had her.

In addition to all these points in her favor, she is as affectionate as a kitten, jealous if I pat her neighbor and overlook her, full of high spirits that frequently produce the most nonsensical capers, possessed of an aristocratic, even royal bearing that places her as undisputed boss of the herd. She rarely makes use of her horns to assert her supremacy, but when she does the demonstration is swift and not soon forgotten. At the same time she is never overbearing or eager to parade her domination. On the contrary, she is one of the herd, not at all class-conscious, until a dispute must be settled. Then she seems to put on her regal robes, sit in judgment and make the decision, confident that there will be no challenge.

And there never is. But once judgment is passed and her queenly duties have been accomplished, she is as likely as not to start a hilarious stampede by prancing about, tail high, and butting imaginary foes, a kind of shadow boxing with horns instead of gloves.

Gaby is a great talker, the only real conversationalist in the herd. She rumbles, chuckles, squeaks, emits plaintive notes as well as joyful ones. I am never too sure what it is all about, but since Gaby talks on regardless of an audience, my understanding makes little difference. I do follow her oral whimsies when she lies down after eating her grain and being milked. Then she mutters and whispers like any human full of good food and at ease in an armchair.

Gaby presented me with a bull the first time, the second time with a heifer, a handsome animal, even more affectionate than her dam and every bit as charming. More than a year must pass, however, before I know whether she possesses the whole list of superior characteristics of which Gaby can boast. One thing is certain. Every heifer Gaby wishes to give me will be cherished. A herd composed of Gaby's offspring could not fail to be a good one—a real combination of business and pleasure.

Toots takes the comedy lead at High Meadows. She has a white face with narrow black rims about her eyes, giving the effect of a couple of shiners acquired during an all-night binge. And her character matches completely her comic face. If Toots were human she would swing her hips boldly, chew gum, speak with a Brooklyn accent, wise-crack on every occasion and be ever ready for a party, with a tendency to become noisy after a couple of drinks. She bears an other-side-of-the-tracks air and makes no attempt to conceal it. Yet she is one of the best cows in the barn.

I bought Toots as a bred heifer at the same time I bought Gaby, two of the best buys I could have made when I knew nothing about judging an animal. She bore a bull calf on schedule and since then has given me two heifers, Bebop and Pixie, who give every indication of continuing the zany qualities of their mother.

Toots invariably manages to add her individual fillip to whatever she does. She goes to her stall as docile as you please, but persists in pushing her head to the side of her stanchion instead of in it. That is to compel me to hold the stanchion at an angle and nudge her, whereupon she pops her head in where it belongs with a triumphant leer for my reward. She is always the last one in the barn, waiting outside until I come over, rub her throat, pat her on the back and tell her she is a lovable dope. She grins at the compliment and trots amiably through the door. The old stanchions in the barn were loose in their joints and the release levers had to be held in place with wooden wedges. Toots became adept at shaking her stanchion until the wedge fell out, then shaking it some more until the lever was released and she was able to step back and roam about at will. She enjoys bedeviling the other cows, not in a mean but rather in a pestering manner—a prod with a horn, a playful butt on the flank, while blatting gleefully at her own jokes.

Toots learned to lift from its socket the drop bar, which prevents entry into the feed alley. Then she would parade up and down before the other cows, just out of reach of any who lunged at her for an avenging prod but were brought up short by the stanchions. She would flirt her tail in their faces, nibble at hay in front of them and laugh throatily at her imprisoned pals. Eventually she would reach the pile of bedding straw at the end of the alley and stretch out in ostentatious comfort, in full view of the others, casting a mocking eye at them.

I have watched Toots at all these tricks by opening the door at unexpected moments. She shows no trace of guilt when caught in her various acts. She merely walks to her stanchion, waits to be tucked in and looks at me as much as to say, "It's your fault for having such rickety stanchions. Don't blame me." So I don't blame her. I would much rather laugh at her. Which I suspect she knows, being a smart girl.

I have on occasion become annoyed by her antics. During the winter I turn the cows out daily, even in very cold weather, to let them stretch and lick themselves. I open the stanchion nearest the door and proceed along the line till all the cows are free. Occasionally I turn around at the end of the barn to find the whole herd milling about, climbing over each other and bellowing. Toots is the cause. She takes a stand at the door, lowers her horns menacingly and holds them all at bay. Except Gaby. Gaby just shoves her aside and goes outdoors. But the others are less daring. So I rush into the melee, yell at Toots, even whack her with a fork handle, and then am invariably obliged to laugh as she kicks up her heels and ducks through the door.

Yes, Toots is a lovable dope. With all her capriciousness, she is one of the most affectionate cows in the herd. She loves to be petted and talked to. If I pay too much attention to her neighbor Gaby she thrashes about until I am compelled to turn to her, when she immediately becomes quiet. All in all, she is obedient, easy to milk and to handle. She has never so much as lifted a foot to kick at me, even when I have had to treat her for painful cuts from barbed wire.

Toots is smaller than Gaby, and I wonder, not knowing her ancestry, whether early breeding prevented her full growth. The size of her daughters when they mature will provide some evidence. Bebop, as a yearling, is at least a good average in size for a Holstein. But if Toots' growth was stunted, no harm seems to have been done to her milk-making ability. She gives about sixty pounds after freshening, drops to fifty pounds after a month or so, and slowly dwindles to thirty pounds at the end of ten months. That gives her an average close to thirty-five pounds for the entire period. And it is the cows that average thirty-five pounds or better, for ten thousand pounds total, that build up the milk check.

Gaby and Toots are four-year-olds. All the others, Maggie and Bella excepted, of course, are younger than four years. This means that their dairy value has still to be proved. Noella is one, however, in whom I place complete confidence. She is Bella's daughter, the first heifer born after I acquired the old herd, and, of course, she became a great pet. She still is as a three-year-old. Whenever we cross a meadow where the cows are pastured, Noella leaves the herd, trots to us and expects to be fondled. If she is in the brook pasture and we go on into the woods, she tags along, preferring to have an arm around her neck but contented just to be with us. If we shoo her back, she looks so forlorn that we have foresworn such measures and let her come along. I'm sure some day she will walk right into the house.

Vicky is the second heifer born in my barn. Her mother was Dolly, big and raw-boned like Maggie but lacking Mag's exceptional qualities. Dolly would start off bravely enough with fifty pounds of milk, but production soon slumped and after a couple of months would be down to thirty pounds. At the end of ten months her average was a scant twenty-five pounds. However, Dolly was old, and her teeth were worn. I kept the two heifers she dropped, Vicky and Bonnie, on the gamble that she had been a better milker in her youth. But I recognized the gamble. Dolly had a dull look in her eye which age could not entirely account for. Maggie was older but showed a brightness in appearance that Dolly lacked. That brightness and alertness must have some relation to vitality—the physical, and, perhaps, mental constitution that assures the health and stamina which, when coupled with Maggie's productivity, make for an outstanding cow.

Vicky has that same dullness in her eye and in her reactions. At times I vow she is stupid. Again I find what can only be described, in a manner of mixed husbandry, as a hangdog appearance. She is quiet, gentle, but with an exaggerated humbleness that holds little appeal. On the other hand, she is a good, though not remarkable, dairy type, with clean lines and a large barrel, broad and strong in the rump.

How much connection there is between general appearance and milk production is hard to define. One point is certain. A good cow usually looks alert. Some poor cows may have that brightness, but I doubt if a

143

good cow ever looks dull. I will know more about that when Vicky is farther along in her second lactation period.

During her first one she started with about thirty-five pounds, held at thirty pounds for a few months, then slipped down to twenty for an average of about twenty-five pounds. After her second calving she improved somewhat on production, but I am keeping my fingers crossed. In any event she has paid off the expense of raising her and, if I do sell her, the price will be clear profit. That is a cold, businesslike attitude which I find I can take only with regard to a cow that does not interest me particularly. I doubt if I could bring myself to sell Gaby, or Toots, or Noella, even if their milk dwindled to a low average. They, by contrast with Vicky, are fun to have around.

Susie, Black-eyed Susan, is my only purebred. I bought her early in 1951 to calve in February. She is an experiment for I am not yet prepared, and may never be, to build a herd of purebreds. I find that good grade Holsteins will produce as much milk as average pure-breds; they are more rugged, less highstrung. But I had sold Hilda, who was too hard to milk, getting $236 for her as beef, and Susie was the best replacement I could find at the time. Her price was $275. She was thin when I brought her to the barn and had not been liberally grained before freshening; I had no great expectations for big milk production at the start. She is now making twenty pounds daily and I am satisfied. I expect her to increase that amount considerably in the next two years, for she comes of good stock. Also I want to keep her

heifers to learn if they, by virtue of good sires and artificial breeding, will do better than Susie.

Susie was nervous and scary. She objected violently
to the milking machine at first, and for two weeks I had
a real battle on my hands just to keep the machine attached to her udder despite her kicking. Once, in exasperation, after replacing the machine several times, I
socked her hard with my open hand. She turned absolutely rigid though the tension within her was such that
she began to tremble from head to tail. Since, obviously,
that kind of treatment would make no progress, I settled
down to patience. I talk to Susie whenever I am near
her; I make a point of petting her, stroking her, getting
her accustomed to my hands. While she is milking I sit
on a stool, talking to her, rubbing her forehead, never
making an abrupt move. It is paying off nicely.

Such is the herd at High Meadows—these that I have
singled out for special mention, and the others: Vicky's
half-sister, Bonnie, affectionate and docile, yet still an
unknown quantity; Judy, a big, sleek, black three-year-
old, bought as a bred heifer; Penny, small, similar to
Toots in size and conformation, and, like many under-
sized humans, carrying a chip on her shoulder; Blondy
and Raki, the two-year-olds born two days apart.

There are also five small fry in the barn, ranging from
eighteen months to three months.

Of these Jeannie, with the dark-brown hair, is an experiment, a cross-breed. I bought her mother, Goldy,
a handsome gold-brown Guernsey, at what seemed to
me the absurd price of $130. Like many Guernseys, she
had unusually long teats, a good five inches in length.
At the time of the sale, however, I paid no attention to

the teats, noting only her general conformation and large udder. But I should have known something was wrong when such a fine animal met with almost no bidders. Now I have learned that long teats are difficult to milk with a machine and also are likely to get stepped on. As it turned out, Goldy milked out fairly easily by machine and after she freshened gave better than forty pounds of rich, golden milk. But eventually she stepped on not only one but two teats. The teats were not gashed open, as frequently happens, but bruised on the ends. A hard swelling formed and almost entirely closed the milk canal.

Milking became an arduous affair. Goldy was wonderfully patient, even when the machine tugged away for twenty minutes and more. Hand milking was beyond my powers; I simply did not have the strength in my hands, and my hands are strong. A veterinarian worked on her without notable success. I used teat dilators—which are inserted into the teat canals between milkings—and they helped a bit. Prolonged use of dilators, however, leads to irritation and infection of the teats. One morning I found Goldy's udder swollen and feverish. I struggled for days with penicillin and streptomycin; but the infection got in her blood, she refused to eat and soon began to lose weight. The only solution was to sell her for beef though I hated to part with her, for we had become fast friends during her illness.

Goldy had been bred to a purebred Holstein bull before I bought her. When she presented me with a heifer calf, I could not resist keeping the beautiful sable creature. So Jeannie joined the herd. Her coat has turned black, and with her four white stockings she is a fine-looking animal, built like her mother. She will remain a Guernsey type with Holstein markings.

A Holstein-Guernsey cross-breed is supposed to produce an animal that gives milk in Holstein quantity with some of the richness of the Guernsey. This is a profitable combination because of the system of grading milk on butterfat content to establish the price to the dairyman. Indeed, this consideration persuades many dairymen to turn to Guernseys or Jerseys, breeds which give less milk than the Holsteins but make up the difference in the premium on richer milk, which can test 4.0 per cent butterfat and more for Guernseys and up to 6.0 per cent for Jerseys, as against 3.5 for Holsteins.

With all this in mind, though I am a staunch champion of the Holstein and have no intention of turning to Guernseys or Jerseys, I decided to keep Jeannie until she had freshened at least twice and see how much milk she produced as well as how high it tested. That information must wait for two years. One objection—perhaps the major one, though I understand further experimentation may disprove it—is that the offspring of a crossbreed tends to revert to one of the two strains and usually with a weakening of the best characteristics of either the dam or the sire. Whether I will carry my experiment to that point will be determined later. But with artificial insemination and the availability of proved sires of the several breeds, fascinating work might lie ahead. Time would be the controlling factor in my case. I would have to wait some four years to learn what Jeannie's first calf, if a heifer, would produce in milk and butterfat. That's a long time . . .

All infant animals are appealing, kittens, puppies, pigs,

lambs, colts. One summer in France I agreed to take care of a baby goat just for the fun of watching it. That kid provided endless amusement any time I wished to play with it, and for years I maintained that a kid was without rival as an entertainer, an extraordinary union of age-old wisdom with puckish youth. Here at High Meadows I have transferred my affections. A calf now rates top billing. I can hang over the rail of a calf pen and watch the inmates by the hour.

A calf can be so extremely busy and get exactly nowhere, so gravely purposeful but without purpose. Everything is tremendously interesting and exciting but nothing is important for long. There is so much to investigate, to sniff, bite, gnaw, shove around. For such a lively mind, concentration is stuffy, suitable for old age, perhaps, but like a chafing hobble to an oversized bump of curiosity and energy that is constantly at the boiling point. That pitchfork handle propped against the pen palings—what could be more wonderful? An intriguing smell, smooth to the tongue, delightful to chew on, too. Not for long, however. That wisp of straw dangling over there is far more inviting. Or that salt block on a bracket. Or the grain pan. Or the drinking cup. Dozens of objects, each more thrilling than the rest. Concentration? What nonsense. And with an awkward, sidewise kick of one hind foot, the calf shows her scorn for concentration and proceeds to examine other novelties. Life is marvelous.

I have three calves at present. Topsy, seven months, and Windy, five months, are in one pen. Adjoining is Pixie, three months.

Topsy is out of Gaby. When she was very young,

her coat was dark brown, like Jeannie's. That reversion to early Holstein ancestry—the original Holstein was red and white, not black and white—was short-lived, however, and Topsy now is black with white hindlegs and white stockings on her forelegs. Otherwise, she has all the trim, dairy-type lines of her mother.

Windy, out of Bella, was born on the night of the tempest of November 25, 1950, hence the name. She is larger and handsomer than either of her half-sisters, Noella and Raki, was at five months. She also is mainly black, marked very similarly to Topsy. The two are like lovebirds, lying down head to head, licking each other, sharing their grain pan without dispute.

Pixie, out of Toots, has a clown's face, one side white, the other black, a circus mask. Her personality is just as divided. At times she presents a sober mien, particularly now that she has started chewing her cud. Lying down, chewing busily, she looks old, a grown cow in miniature. Suddenly, as though she had been touched by a charged wire, sobriety vanishes—the cud too, momentarily. She leaps to her feet and starts a wild round of galloping and kicking, usually winding up with a head-on attack against the cornerpost of the pen. For a half-hour or more she is an infant, intently occupied in every direction, until old age settles upon her once again, whereupon the cud pops up and she resembles once again a staid old cow.

All my animals are docile for the most part, but so varied in temperament, so bursting with spirits, that I am always prepared for the unexpected. Anything can happen—now and then it does, causing extra work, profanity, and loud avowals that cows are the most irritating animals in creation. My temper soon cools, however. I look at the row of faces turned in my direction, some grinning, some registering surprise, but never a hint of humbleness; and, of course, I give in, smile back at them and announce that they are the most wonderful cows on earth.

CHAPTER 10

IN THE HERD OF SEVENTEEN HEAD AT HIGH Meadows, there are now only two of the original batch of bossies that were both my guinea pigs and my teachers in dairy farming. I am hoping—even betting when optimism soars—that I shall acquire two more heifer calves from Maggie and Noella. Nineteen head, twenty at the most, are all I care to handle. At any rate, I keep insisting to myself that twenty must be the maximum. But I don't always look myself straight in the eye while insisting. I avoid being pinned down to a definite promise. After all, Gaby and Toots and Bella might produce heifers next winter. Maggie and Bella might defy age by continuing to pour out pails of milk. Then which ones will I be able to part with? My predicament will be grave.

Four years have brought many changes in the herd. Old cows could be disposed of because I could convince myself it was an act of mercy. Young cows purchased during those years that failed to fulfill expectations could be sold without great regret because my attachment to them had not fully developed. Now, however, with the exception of Susie, the purebred, I have labored and lived with them for more than a year in every instance. And ten of the seventeen I have helped to bring into the world, coddled, played with and watched grow their every inch. Affection now runs almost too deep to be wrenched out and sent off in a livestock dealer's truck.

Nevertheless, I have brought myself to one decision on which I believe I can stand firm. I will get rid of a cow that becomes incurably hard to milk or hard to manage. Such an animal can deflate my morale as well as my ego if I am forced to admit that every kind of effort and patience has been fruitless. When all goes well, within reasonable expectations, I find milking a pleasure, not a chore. It is a pastime, a form of recreation, like batting out flies to Scoop or walking in the woods. A difficult cow not only mars that pleasure but also builds up a fixation in me until I no longer look forward to my two daily trips to the barn.

Dora, one of the eight cows I started with, was such an animal. A big, good-looking cow, she had a sullen, suspicious eye. After being hit several times by her lightning punch with either hind foot, I turned, as usual, to Richard for advice. He told me something of Dora's history, though he couldn't be sure whether Dora had been born mean or had acquired meanness. Personally I doubt that any cow is so innately bad-tempered that she cannot be cured. Anyway, Dora hated dogs and almost certainly had been chased and tormented by them. This had produced, or enhanced, a tendency to kick. One owner had tried to beat this tendency out of her. He had merely succeeded in making her extremely nervous and more artful with her blows. She developed speed, precision and a delivery that never telegraphed its beginning.

The same owner resorted to hobbles. Every time he milked her he hobbled her hind feet. This kept both hooves on the ground but, of course, merely increased Dora's urge to let fly when she was free to do so. Before I acquired her she had been in the herd of Arnold, Richard's son, a born dairyman. He had promptly tossed the hobbles into the junk barrel and by stern patience had made some progress toward making Dora a more tractable cow.

When I took over Dora I also voted against hobbles, though I admit that black-and-blue bruises on my forearm occasionally made me long for them. Nevertheless, I stuck to my resolution and regarded Dora as a psychopathic case that could be cured by proper treatment. Thus I maintained my interest though I failed to develop any liking for my patient. She was so thoroughly unpredictable. After much petting, great care never to make a sudden, unexpected movement and a good deal of quiet talk, she would submit to milking without a gesture of complaint. Whereupon I would be vastly cheered, certain that I was making progress. Then, for no reason I could discern, she would let fly with that devastating jab, a short one, loaded with dynamite. And once the kick had been delivered, she would stiffen all over, ready for the expected wallop with a club or the sharp tines of a pitchfork.

153

I vow she was disappointed when punishment was not forthcoming. She had reached the stage where pain was welcome justification for her next attack. Without it, she was befuddled. Once, as I started to attach the machine, I fell over backwards from the stool—not at all an unusual occurrence for me in the early days. Dora figured that in some way she was responsible or else enjoyed my mishap so much that she was glad to take responsibility for it. She tensed from tail to muzzle, awaiting a blow. I assembled myself, disregarded her marble-like immobility and again started to attach the machine. I am positive she was infuriated because I did not swat her; for the moment I was in position and, before the machine had touched her, she let loose and landed squarely on my forearm. Once more she braced for the blow. I slapped the machine onto her udder and walked away. Apparently she was too confused to move for she stood still until I returned, removed the machine and went to the next cow, all the while noting an absolutely baleful look in her eye.

Milking was not exactly a pleasure at first, but what fun there was in it was overshadowed by the knowledge that morning and night I had to confront Dora and be prepared for the worst. So I sold her for beef, admitting my defeat but more than glad to be rid of her.

Hilda was my other problem cow. If she had had braids wound about her head she would have looked like a German fraulein. Her eyes, her solid body and a kind of saccharine gentleness all bore out the Teutonic resemblance—hence her name. I bought Hilda as a three-year-old from a good herd and paid the high price, for the time, of $365 because I wanted a cow very much, liked her appearance, and, when the bidding became brisk, got just as stubborn as two other farmers who liked her.

Hilda was a good cow, gave good milk and was extremely easy to manage. She was also a coward. It was a trait quickly recognized by the rest of my herd, who bullied Hilda without cease so that she came to remain apart from the others. I sided with Hilda in this situation, doing my best to comfort her. As she became gradually more difficult to milk, I leaned to the belief that she had developed a fear or dread complex that inhibited her from letting her milk down. This actually may have been the source of some of her difficulty, but it was not the entire cause.

Hilda's teats, from the start, had tight sphincter muscles, which close the milk canal at the teat tip, thus holding the milk until stimulation causes the cow to "let down" her milk and the milking act is quickly accomplished. In Hilda's case they also grew increasingly muscular, not larger but firmer. The combination eventually became too much for the machine, whose pressure is surprisingly strong, to say nothing of human hands. Normally a cow should milk out, with the machine, in three to five minutes. The time for Hilda steadily lengthened during the more than two years that I had her. I finally clocked her at twenty long minutes.

The veterinarian had "peeled" each teat—a quick operation with a tube carrying a tiny blade in a slot. The blade remains in the slot when the tube is inserted in the teat canal, and protrudes when the tube is withdrawn, thus slicing away hard tissue that may have formed. The operation was of little help. I massaged

155

Hilda's udder with a warm towel just before milking her to assist her in letting down her milk. The result was negligible. I tried dilators. But Hilda continued to lose against my watch. And I began to lose hope. I came to dread milking her, gentle and uncomplaining though she was. Twenty minutes is not a long time, and I had no obligation to hurry, but the knowledge that my other cows required only a few minutes to milk out made those twenty minutes of sitting on a stool the most irksome period of my entire day. So, sorry though I was—for I was fond of Hilda—I sold her.

The change in my attitude toward milking was so pronounced that I promptly made my vow that I would get rid of any cow that was hard to milk. And I intend to keep that vow. I know farmers with cows that flatly refuse to be milked by machine. I will have none of them, superior animals though they may be. I know farmers who would continue to struggle with another Hilda. Not me. Milking can be fun and I propose to keep it that way with cows that start to let down their milk when they spy the machine and get the job over with in a hurry so that they, and I, can assume a horizontal position.

Hilda was hard to part with, Dora was not. Goldy, though I owned her for only a few months, was harder to give up than Hilda, for she was an intelligent, sensitive creature, whose deep violet eyes were bottomless wells of feeling and understanding. Nellie's going, however, caused an ache that lasted for days and I still catch myself looking for her big white head and body, with just a peppering of black, when I count the herd as I bring them to the barn in the soft obscurity of dawn.

Grandma Nellie came with the place. She was old then, with one quarter of her udder slack from careless handling. Yet the other three quarters gave good milk, more than forty pounds when she was fresh; when younger she had given sixty pounds, which promised well for her daughters. After a first bull calf Nellie gave me Blondy, who now is living up to her mother's reputation. Though a bosom pal of stodgy Bella, Nellie was far more responsive and affectionate and soon became the pet of the herd. She was the first one to show complete faith in me, to accept treatment for a minor injury that made her wince but never lift a foot in protest. She had a superbly youthful spirit, ready for a game with the younger ones, frequently cavorting with remarkable agility when she found it so good to be alive that a dance was the one way to express her joy.

However, her teeth were worn to stubs and she was no longer able to conceive; her fate was obvious. The decision came hard. It was like ridding the house of an infirm but honored member of the family. I felt guilty, as though I were committing an underhanded act, to shatter abruptly all the confidence that had been built up day by day for two years by calling in a dealer, coldly accepting money and leading her into a van. There dread would replace the security and tranquillity she had accepted as permanent. Cows may not follow the same thought patterns that men do, but I know how sensitive they can be and I am positive Grandma Nellie was filled with dark forebodings, even terror, during the journey from my barn to the slaughterhouse.

I gained a new conception of Nellie's intelligence the morning I kept her in her stanchion awaiting the dealer.

She had been kept in the barn alone before, and she had protested her solitude with intermittent bawling. But she had not been suspicious and uneasy as on that last morning. She showed her agitation by tossing her head, fidgeting nervously. While I cleaned the barn she eyed me closely, following every move, pleading for release from the stanchion and her horrid thoughts. She became quiet while I stood beside her and talked, though it was beyond me to lie by telling her she would soon be out in the meadow with her pals. About all I could say was "Take it easy," along with dull-sounding words of affection.

I went on with chores until I could no longer stand the impact of those soft, trusting eyes narrowed slightly by troubling premonitions. I fetched a forkful of clover hay, reserved for the young heifers, and a big scoopful of grain, hoping to keep her occupied and to allay her worries. That was an error. Such unaccustomed attention fortified her suspicions and her nervousness increased. Even the routine ear-scratching was resented, as much as to say, "You can't fool me, you're hiding bad news."

During the first war, when horses, not machines, furnished most of the locomotive power, I encountered artillery horses that smelled death. They were habituated to the din of bursting shells, of machine guns and rifles, to the shrill commands and confusion that marked a surprise attack by the enemy. As a rule they could be relied upon to wheel a .75 cannon into position with the same efficiency as on parade grounds. But occasionally they sensed impending disaster; they caught the smell of death in their flaring nostrils. Then a horse would stop in its tracks, mindless of whips and curses, nose raised to sift the air for a strange and ominous odor. A mad squeal of terror would rise above the surrounding pandemonium, an unearthly moaning wail in answer to an awful warning that death was near.

Well, I am sure Nellie was suddenly aware that death was close. She made no outcry but she stopped fidgeting, tested the air with her big moist muzzle and gazed wonderingly into space, alert to some incomprehensible presence.

It was too much for me. I left the barn and leaned against a gatepost. For a moment I was ready to open the stanchion and turn her loose. Several times before, however, I had weakened regarding Nellie, though I knew I was merely delaying an act that was unavoidable. So I climbed aboard the manure wagon and drove to East Meadow, far from the barn.

When I returned the dealer had arrived. We agreed hurriedly upon a price. I smacked Nellie on the flank with old-time heartiness, but my throat was too tight for conversation. She walked calmly to the truck, resigned, perhaps, because now she understood what was in store. Then she was gone and all I had in place of her was a miserable handful of money. Except for the memory of Nellie, which can withstand the erosion of many years.

Since the going of Grandma Nellie, I am recurrently haunted by the thought that some day I must part with Maggie. One, two, possibly three years may intervene before that unwelcome day, but the outcome is inescapable. That wonderful mechanism must run down as age preys on joints and organs. Nevertheless, I do my utmost to shove the thought out of mind or bury it beneath a host of other thoughts I hasten to pile over it. I simply don't believe I can bear up under the strain of that farewell. For Maggie will know, more surely than Nellie, that doom impends; and to see fear in those old eyes that have looked at me so long with serene faith in whatever I decide would be too much. Of one thing I am certain —I will not be present when the dealer arrives. Someone else will have to dicker about the money and aid in getting her into the truck.

There is one solution I have been considering. I could dig a pit in one of the meadows. Maggie could be led to it, with the rest of the herd nearby so that no suspicion would be aroused. Then, before premonition of an unusual occurrence—in fact with her peace of mind completely undisturbed—a .45 automatic at the temple would bring a quick and painless finish. Quicklime and a blanket of earth would do the rest. And there would be the assurance that up to the very end, to the very last split second, Maggie had found life extremely pleasant. That might dispose of nightmarish thoughts.

Some day I may be shown in grievous error but I maintain, self-flattery or no, that my cows find life at High Meadows sufficiently to their liking to vitiate any real desire to roam afar. They have reasonably good pasture even in the driest spells; they are moved from one meadow to another for variety; cool shade in the woods is available when the sun is hottest. I pass them at least once a day in addition to fetching them for milking. I call to them, stop and talk a moment. And thus far I have had very little difficulty with the fence problem.

Not that High Meadows is bereft of fences. The

stone walls are mostly intact where they were first built
—a labor that perpetually astounds me. (Local authority
declares that a good worker could lay five rods, or eighty
feet, of those walls in a day. The very thought makes
my back ache.) Barbed wire is needed, however, to fill
in gaps, particularly along the boundary lines through
the woods. The wire fencing was already becoming
decrepit when I took over. Many of the posts were
rotted and, if erect, were held that way by the wire,
providing an illusory barrier which collapsed at the first
push.

I confess I banked on the illusion far more than a real
farmer should. I cut a few posts and stuck them in places
where the sagging wire was an open invitation to wander. I restrung wire where staples had pulled out of
rotting posts. But I knew there were wide openings deep
in the woods where trees had fallen across the wire or
posts had simply become non-existent. So until I found
time for repairing these large gaps, I hoped my cows
would not penetrate that far into the woods.

The original herd, long familiar with the whole farm
and probably convinced by previous escapades that
browsing was extremely skimpy deep in the woods, gave
me no trouble. They stayed where I put them or, if they
did occasionally find a hole, I promptly plugged it.
When my young stock was big enough to turn out with
the older cows, however, the situation altered. They
were more venturesome, filled with an explorer's zeal.
If they did not find holes in a fence, they worried re-
straining wire until it gave way. When they started to
hightail about beyond the supposed barrier, the old cows,
their curiosity piqued, were not long in following, more

sedately but willing to investigate a change of scenery.

Even so, I was not greatly bothered. They never strayed far and were easy to head back to where they belonged, especially the older ones; and once they were started in the right direction the heifers, afraid they might miss something, soon tagged after. Except on two occasions, and only one of those was due to my lackadaisical fencing.

There is a flagstone quarry in the northeast corner of the farm, so secluded in the woods that I was willing to lease it when a neighbor proposed working it. Other persons have made bids to thin out the woods by cutting smaller growth for mine props, even to cut the big hemlocks, beech, ash and hard maple, and some have sought to cart away sections of the stone walls for fireplaces, chimneys and similar construction. I have refused such bids, at once and finally. For the present at least I have a fondness for every single tree on the place. Removing flagstone, which I like to see used, from a hilltop almost devoid of trees, struck me as another matter.

The road to the quarry leads through the eastern edge of my brook pasture, where I turn out my heifers and dry cows for the summer. The quarry workers, of course, agreed to keep gates closed and to watch the fencing. One day, however, they took down some wire on the rim of the quarry to facilitate work, and left it down for the night. Naturally, three of my heifers off on a tour discovered the opening and went gaily on their way.

I glance at the pasture several times a day when stock is there and almost without fail glimpse the animals, count them and feel reassured. Thus it was that I spotted

the dry cows, but noted that three heifers were absent
—the two irresponsibles, Blondy and Raki, and young
Bonnie. I started on a tour of my own, finally reached
the quarry without finding trace of them, learned the
wire had been down, found tracks in some soft ground
and went in pursuit. I found them at last in a neighbor's
pasture, quietly browsing with a number of his heifers
and dry cows. Evidently they had jumped or clambered
over the stone wall bounding the pasture, for I could
find no opening. They recognized me when I called,
Bonnie and Raki ambled over to say hello, and, though
I had no lead rope, I started to plan on herding them
back.

The bovine mind works in strange ways. Once habit
is ingrained, it will stick to that habit with fair predictability. But predictability is reduced to zero when a
new situation arises. A cow refuses, with consummate
stubbornness, to be pushed into anything unfamiliar.
She can be led and coaxed with infinite patience, tact
and an occasional whack, though success may be frus-
trated at the last moment when some quirk in her mind
sends her off on an unexpected tangent. Then the whole
game begins again, until another quirk occurs.

Loss of temper avails nothing. Yowls of exasperation
and too many whacks cause the cow to brace all four
legs; she becomes as immovable as a locomotive off its
rails. In fact, as a lesson in self-control, I know of nothing to equal the job of herding home two or three heifers.

My renegade trio knew me and showed no alarm
when I walked up to them, though not many dairymen
can do that with their young stock. As they had stayed

close to each other in the new herd, I had no great difficulty in separating them from the others and starting them toward a gate that gave onto a road which, once on it, they would pretty much have to follow unless they found an opening into another meadow. They took their time, now nipping at grass here and there, now gazing into space, but finally arrived close to the gate. I walked quietly to the gate to open it; but although as a rule an open gate is an invitation to adventure immediately accepted, my heifers now evinced no interest. When I turned back to drive them through they tossed their heads in derision and ambled back to the herd.

I risked leaving the gate open and went back. This time the whole herd became curious; and when my three were headed for the gate, all the others decided to join the game, prancing about like kids out of school. To avert a catastrophe I was obliged to run at top speed, circling wide around the herd, to get to the gate first. I just made it, completely blown, and looked with no friendly eye on all the inquisitive faces before me, ready for another game.

After three more equally unsuccessful tries I was worn out. At my age I have no aspirations to train for cross-country honors. So I decided I needed help. The following morning I returned with a young neighbor. Each of us had lead ropes, and we were fresh, ready for the fray. Five hours later we were back at High Meadows, with the heifers, but I had to lie on the grass for a half-hour to convince myself my legs were not made of rubber.

We got ropes on the noses of Raki and Bonnie. They were coaxed, pushed and pulled toward the nearest gate, which led to the farmer's barn and on to another road. Blondy hung about, suspicious, sending telepathic messages to her pals to have no part in such proceedings. Nevertheless, we got Bonnie through the gate and tied her to a tree. Then after a long tugging match, Raki went through. Once more, the other cows gathered about the gate, knowing it led to their barn and perhaps some grain. Chasing them away was futile, for they moved right back. So my friend manned the gate, prepared to swing it open when I drove Blondy close to it, then slam it closed to the others.

Three times I nursed Blondy up to the gate, it opened hospitably, and three times Blondy lifted her tail and dove through the group of spectators. The fourth time, however, by great good luck, she went through, headed for the road and bawling for her pals to follow. Raki fought her rope, slipped it off her nose and went after Blondy.

Eventually we were all on the road and the rest of the journey promised to be fairly easy. I kept Blondy and Raki close to Bonnie, whose rope was held by my friend. All went smoothly until we came to a tenant house. There the tenant's wife and two children and a small dog were on the lawn. My heifers revealed an immediate distaste for such an audience. The woman, instead of going into or behind the house with children and dog, squatted down in an attempt to be inconspicuous. That really did alarm my heifers. They tried to turn back, but I plied a switch with vigor and checked them. So they balked, refusing to budge in any direction—whereupon the dog began to dash about, yapping its head off.

That was too much for Blondy. From a standing start

she cleared a four-strand wire fence and galloped toward the far side of a huge meadow. I exploded with wrath and discouragement. For this I was roundly scolded by the woman, who was still shrilling away when I climbed the fence and took off after Blondy, leaving my friend to get along as best he could. He was lucky. The woman finally realized that she should disappear from the scenery along with her unpleasant dog, and Raki and Bonnie were back home long before I was with Blondy.

The meadow was vast, boggy from recent rains, and the gate to the road was far back toward the main house. Blondy showed no inclination for going in that direction. All I could do was trail along after her, up to my ankles in sticky mud, and slowly maneuver her along the fence till we reached the gate. I called on all the gods to steer Blondy to the left and not the right. If she had turned right, deciding she wanted to rejoin the herd we had taken her from, I probably would have sat down and wept. But she turned left. We passed the house with no one visible. We arrived at the road leading to my farm and Blondy was turned in there without difficulty. From there on I foresaw no trouble. But Blondy still had a trick to win. She was bent on a grand slam, whether I liked it or not.

There is a strip of dense undergrowth along one side of the road. Fifty yards within it, an old stone wall runs up a rocky slope to another wall which extends out to the road. Blondy voted to leave the road and go through that jungle of whipping branches, snarled grapevines and slippery rocks. And I could only follow, keeping her in the general direction of home.

That was an arduous half-hour. Blondy was completely unconcerned, probably enjoying herself and the occasional mouthfuls of leaves she shucked off on the way. I was utterly weary and furious, but loud curses might have provided just the incentive Blondy needed to start running. She could navigate through the tangle of brush much faster than I. So I summoned all the discipline I possessed and puffed and wheezed on her heels until we reached the road once again and started anew for the house. This time we arrived, Blondy as fresh as though she had roused from a nap, I as completely beaten as ever in my life. All the profanity I had held back, stored up for hours, should have come out in a long and echoing blast. My best effort was a brief, weak sputter like that of a squib firecracker.

The other escapade involved the whole herd, alerted the countryside and again left me weary to the point of collapse. I had myself to blame.

Failure to check a corner of fence in a small grove of hemlocks was my undoing. I knew the cows liked the spot, for it was wonderfully cool in the dense shade and the hemlock needles made an inviting bed. Beyond the fence was a thicket of brambles and saplings so lacking in grazing possibilities that I could hardly believe the cows would try to penetrate it. Cows, alas, have a bump of curiosity whose dimensions I apparently never will be able to appreciate.

I had elected to varnish the kitchen floor. I planned to apply one coat in the morning and a second in the evening. My intention was to finish with evening milking as early as possible, have dinner, then complete my varnishing. It all fitted very neatly.

Just before five o'clock I headed for the woods pasture on the south ridge, calling my bovine pets. But there was no responding moo, not even a dead branch crackling as they moved about. I visited their usual haunts and found no trace, not even fresh droppings. I penetrated deeper into the woods toward the south boundary, where I knew my fence was weak. A post was down in one place, and I prowled about on my neighbor's land, finding the going rough through underbrush and tangled fallen trees. Still there was no track or sign of my cows. Hot and tired, I noted that the time was six-thirty and thought of the floor I wanted to finish so that I could use the kitchen the next day. Finally I decided the smart thing to do would be to return to the house, get on with the varnishing, and rely on the cows to come to the barn before dark, thirsty and ready to be milked.

When I was half through varnishing, Richard's daughter drove up and announced that some of my cows were in Uncle Gaylord's barn, Uncle Gaylord being Richard's brother, who owns the farm north of mine. But I was so convinced that my herd had headed south that I couldn't believe those strays belonged to me. Moreover, I couldn't figure out how they had got there from my woods pasture. However, I dumped my brush in turpentine, got in the car and went visiting. Sure enough, five of my animals, including old Maggie, were in stanchions in Gaylord's barn, looking a bit frayed from long hiking but glad to see me.

Gaylord told me three others had been seen in one of his far meadows. That made eight, and six were still to be accounted for. By that time it was beginning to get dark, and I was truly anxious about my wanderers. If they got on a road at night they might get hit by a passing car or truck; otherwise they would keep moving along and be miles away by morning. I hurried off over lumpy ground, through mudholes, and over stone fences and finally picked up one heifer. She was definitely worried at being alone in strange parts, so worried, in fact, that she came along with me like a homeless pup and joined the others in Gaylord's barn. Gaylord, meanwhile, had been kind enough to milk the five there, and they had perked up considerably.

While I was deciding where to look next, shouts came from my house across the rolling fields a half-mile away. The voice was Richard's telling me to come back. Now the problem was to drive six cows along a dark road and up to my mountain. Gaylord offered to help, using his car once the animals were started along the road. In the glare of the headlights they all looked tired, plodding at a slow pace, but Maggie was worn out. She had calved only two weeks before; her udder was enormous, even though milked out, and slapped hamperingly against her hind legs. I was tired too, but somehow I couldn't persuade myself to ride in a car while Old Mag was obliged to trudge on foot, her weak pasterns ready to snap, I was convinced, at any moment. So Gaylord drove and I walked with Maggie, trying to keep her spirits high.

I am still amazed that she managed to climb the mountain. But she knew she was headed for home. Nonetheless there were moments when she was compelled to stop on that steep road to regain strength while I braced her from behind to keep her from losing ground. Eventually we all reached the barn, and Maggie went to her stanchion and flopped down with an explosive sigh of relief, as though another step would have been beyond her powers.

Six more of my cows were home to greet me when I drooped wearily on a milkstool. Richard told me another neighbor to the east of my farm had found them, decided they were mine and telephoned Richard. I, of course, have no phone. Then he had herded them up to my barn. Still there were two absent, Gaby and Judy. A few minutes later, Richard's daughter again arrived, with word that my two waifs were safe in still another neighbor's barn where they could remain for the night. The hour being close to eleven o'clock, the only thing to do was to leave them there. Pending my arrival with Gaylord, Richard had milked the six that had been brought in.

I was too worn out then to appreciate what neighbors had done for me on that disturbing night. It was one of several examples I have witnessed of rural spirit, the readiness to pitch in and help when trouble comes. Four neighbors had done their utmost to make sure my cows were kept from harm or brought home; two neighbors had milked them while I scoured the countryside, and they all had passed it off with jokes at my expense when I thanked them. I was so bucked up by the outcome that when I was alone in the house again, I brought out the paint brush and finished varnishing the kitchen floor before crawling upstairs and falling into bed with a moan almost as loud as Maggie's.

I brought Gaby and Judy home the following morning with their complete co-operation. They trotted along ahead of me, plainly eager to get back on familiar ground with their pals. Also, they had not been milked since the previous morning (my neighbor feared I might be annoyed if a stranger milked my cows) and wanted to be eased of the abnormal tension in their udders. After milking them I turned them out to join the others, and great commotion ensued as the whole herd huddled together and recounted the many details of the escapade.

The best reunion I have witnessed occurred the previous year. The young stock and dry cows were in the brook pasture across the road; the milking cows were in South Meadow beyond the barn, the straight lane passing the house connecting the two. One evening about twilight I glanced out a living-room window and saw all the young ones leading a joyous parade along the lane, the dry cows frisking most undignifiedly with the adolescents. They had managed to worry bars loose from the gate and were headed for a festive get-together with the milkers.

I could have driven them back, with considerable effort, and that was my intention when I rushed out the door. But they had so much the air of kids off for the swimming hole that intervening was beyond me. Instead, I let them get close to the gate into the meadow, then opened it and shooed them in.

They needed no urging. In they went, tails aloft, heels kicking, with snorts of merry greeting. The milkers looked up, emitted loud whoops to the effect that "company is here," and started zigzagging down the slope with that stiff-legged half-gallop so ludicrous in cows. Their pleasure was unmistakable. Old Grandma Nellie pranced like a yearling. Big Maggie, who is slow motion incarnate, broke into an awkward trot, her great udder swaying like the basket on a freed balloon.

Such a session of nose-rubbing, of shoving, of exchanges of affectionate licks with rasp-like tongues! Noella and Vicky walked off side by side for all the world like two schoolgirls whispering secrets. Toots and Gaby came as close to kissing as cows ever will. Bella singled out Noella, her daughter, to administer several sharp butts, in typical mother-to-daughter fashion to demonstrate where authority lay.

Excitement ran high until darkness became so thick that I left my gatepost. The cows were only ghostly white shapes milling about. Gossiping probably continued through most of the night.

The herd has its social code, rigid in a few instances, sufficiently elastic otherwise to cope with assorted personalities, individual idiosyncrasies, youth and age. As I have said, Gaby's queenship is firmly established. Obstreperous youngsters such as Bebop are accorded liberties with their rough-housing until liberty becomes license. Then discipline is swift and supposedly harsh enough to impress the rambunctious one with the evils of excess. Bebop and the others, however, soon recover from their bovine spanking and are back at their pranks.

With Hilda gone, Penny is the only isolationist left, though she is gradually merging more and more with the herd. She is not faint-hearted as Hilda was, retorts gamely and effectively if she is being bullied.

The striking part of this communal life is the absence of bad temper. Anger may flare momentarily, but it subsides equally fast. Enmities never develop, grudges are not nursed. No matter how grave the infraction of the code, serenity returns a few minutes later and, if cows smile, which I believe they do, they are all smiling at each other with the best camaraderie. It is this unfailing good nature that lends such appeal to a cow.

After the first day in this new world, a calf is accustomed to my presence and my voice. Thereafter I am expected to provide play, a shirt to chew on, a hand to lick, as well as feed. I have reached into a pen to pet a calf lying down and as close to sleep as a cow gets, for I have yet to find one with her eyes completely closed. Immediately it is alert, on its feet and ready for a romp. Only loud, unexpected noises or unwarranted roughness and cruelty warp its eternal cheerfulness. With good treatment, a calf, or a cow, is never *cowed*. The dictionary to the contrary, *cowed* is wrongly derived. Though beaten day after day she would still find an opportunity for loosing a lightning kick to prove her spirit was strong.

The three cats that prefer the barn to the house have long been accepted as pals by the herd. They dash about beneath the cows, sample beet pulp and grain from one and all without a flicker of protest, and submit heroically to frequent baths from those dripping tongues that flatten the cats to the floor and completely envelop the periodical kittens that I come upon in the hay mows or odd corners and which I fetch to cavort before the cows as soon as their legs permit.

Final proof of even temper came with the acceptance of Susquie, my idea of a perfect farm dog. I acquired Susquie from a storekeeper just after I arrived at the farm. Then a month old, the tawny, round ball was half Police, half Dobermann-Pinscher, and gave little

promise of attaining the stature of either one. Today
he weighs ninety pounds and has much the appearance
of a Police dog. He was named in honor of the county
we live in, on the theory that some day he would have
a mate whom we would dub Hannah.

I have made no attempt to train Susquie as a cowdog.
Even the best of the breed are likely to chase cows when
unobserved, and the mere fact that they are used to
drive the cows to the barn revives in the cows a deeply-
rooted dread of dogs as natural enemies.

My cows were openly suspicious of Susquie from the
time he began to tag along with me across the meadows
and in the barn. If he came close to them, they lowered
their heads and jabbed their horns at him. But Susquie
is pretty good-natured also, and to chase about with
high-spirited heifers became an ambition. So he hung
about with them, never thinking of nipping at pasterns
or swinging on a tail. Eventually the old, instinctive
feud simmered down and now has disappeared. The
cows pay no attention when he comes sniffing about,
even lick his nose, which pleases him; and when the urge
to stampede becomes overpowering, one cow stiffens
her tail straight out like a beanpole, another follows suit,
another tail goes up till all are high, and the entire herd
takes off on a wild, bucking, lunging pursuit of ghostly
quarry, then Susquie is in rapture, rushing about amid
hoofs and horns that will do him no harm.

So the cats, the kittens and the dog belong to the herd.
So do we, the family. They know us all, welcome us
to their company. In fact, my wife still gets a welcome
that is too strenuous for her. The first autumn she com-
mitted the error, if it be an error, of fetching a bag of

apples every evening and tossing them over the stone wall to the cows. This kind of human-borne manna was like chewing-gum to French and Italian kids during the war. The treat became a fixture on the bovine calendar, to the point that they assembled eagerly at the gate every evening and were loath to go to the barn if apples were not provided.

In later autumns the apple festival has been less regular for various reasons, with gaps of a week or more between parties. The cows lost the habit of gathering at the gate. Nevertheless, Bossy's memory is long and any time my wife enters a meadow where the cows are pastured, they descend upon her and form a close circle, each shouldering the others to be first for that well-remembered apple. Their zeal is such that the whilom apple-bearer is subjected to a lot of shoving around. But no harm is meant; she manages to get free and waves good-bye, while the cows look puzzled and roll the memory of apple flavor on their tongues.

CHAPTER 11

"SHE'S IN GOOD RIG" IS A POPULAR EXPRESSION among dairymen in these parts. Implying a compliment to the owner of the cow, it is not used freely, for dairymen are not given to empty praise. A cow "in good rig" is thrifty, in good flesh, well cared for and in excellent health.

Maintaining a herd "in good rig" actually sums up the entire problem of dairying. If a cow has an ancestry good enough to endow her with the ability to produce milk in quantity, health is thereafter the controlling factor. A healthy cow makes milk, eats with good appetite, is resistant, if not immune, to most bovine maladies, calves as a rule without difficulty and produces lusty offspring.

Books on dairying gave me the fundamental principles, theoretical and practical, of herd management. Richard and other dairymen have shared their practical knowledge and still are doing so as new problems arise. I have even gained sufficient experience to do a little experimenting of my own, though never anything so drastic as to risk upsetting my cows' health.

Fixed routine is extremely important—punctual milking periods and a feeding schedule closely adhered to both as to time and kind of feed. Good dairymen seldom are early or late in getting to the barn for their milking, though each may have a different time for the job. The time of milking is far less important than sticking to the same time day after day. Nevertheless, occasional lapses have no noticeable effect on Bossy. When Gaby and Judy went astray with the rest of my herd and were sheltered in a neighbor's barn overnight, they were not milked for more than twenty-four hours, yet were back in usual stride as soon as the customary routine was resumed.

I have heard many dairymen of the old-school type argue vociferously that the semi-annual changes to and from daylight saving time, with the loss or gain of one hour, is upsetting to cows. Some even refuse to change their clocks and continue on standard time. Yet I have seen these same farmers attending a livestock sale and delaying departure for an hour or more until a particularly choice cow was put on the block. I'm sure their own animals noticed their tardiness only by bawling hungrily for supper. Certainly the change in time has meant no more to my cows than a little extra milk if an hour was lost, a little less milk if it was gained. Otherwise, I hold strictly to schedule.

Probably no two dairymen feed their stock in like manner or with the same feed. Each has ideas and habits of his own, but if he is intelligent and uses proper feed, his results in milk will be as good as the next one's. The point is that he is consistent in what he feeds and when.

Comfortable quarters obviously contribute to a cow's health. Given adequate room for lying down, with clean bedding, she will get the repose she needs while her milk-making machinery functions. She also will stay surprisingly clean, for the cow is not a dirty animal by nature any more than a pig is. A sufficient dry period likewise is important to a cow's health, for the milk organs need, and deserve, an annual vacation. Breeding at the proper time also plays a part in maintaining health. Once understood, all these phases of dairying are so logical, so much a matter of common sense, that holding to them becomes automatic.

Here is a general outline of my routine, which thus far has been successful—and I see no reason why it should not continue to be so.

Two months before one of my cows is due to freshen I start to dry her off. All grain feeding is stopped abruptly. If she is producing a fair quantity of milk, I also reduce or eliminate the feeding of beet pulp. I may even reduce the amount of hay. If she is on pasture I may keep her in the barn for several days, trying not to hear her bellows of protest, and feed her a limited hay ration. For two days after reducing her feed I milk her twice daily as usual. Then I stop milking her. A day or two later I feel her udder and, if it holds more than three or four quarts of milk, I milk her out. A smaller quantity will be absorbed into her body. Then she has been "dried off."

For the first of the two months, her ration is straight

hay or pasture, all she requires to keep in good flesh. If she is on pasture I put her with the non-milking heifers and merely keep an occasional eye on her. In winter, when the cows are indoors, I know she will snitch a bit of grain from her enstanchioned neighbors, no matter how far to one side I place it, but it will not be enough to matter and it gives her a feeling of triumph over me that keeps her in better temper.

At the start of the second month, Bossy begins to get some beet pulp and a handful of grain in addition to a full hay allotment. The pulp and grain ration is increased day by day to reach a full feed of pulp within a week and about six pounds of grain by the end of two weeks.

Most dairymen feed a grain mixture called "fitting ration" at this time, the idea being to "fit" the cow for calving. For the past two years I have experimented with the same dairy feed I give the milking cows. I figured this way. Since my cows are in good flesh when they are dried off, they do not actually need a fitting ration, the purpose of which is to put meat on cows in poor condition. Also, it is too lean a mixture to make milk. Dairy feed, on the other hand, provides body sustenance and at the same time, being rich in proteins, makes milk. Thus I maintain the cow in prime condition during the ninth month of pregnancy when the unborn calf is making heaviest demands on her and also stimulate her milk-making proclivities. I can't prove that this is true. A prolonged experiment with a number of cows would be necessary to establish reliable figures. But it seems to work and, after all, can't do any harm.

Four weeks before calving I squeeze a bit of milk from each of the cow's four quarters to make sure that no mastitis infection occurred during the drying off. If there is any, I treat the quarter with the new penicillin-streptomycin ointment which can be injected through the teat and massaged into the quarter. The treated quarter is examined daily to assure a cure before milk begins to form in quantity and, if the infection does not clear in three or four days, another dose is given. This usually suffices. (I shall have more to say about mastitis later.)

During the last ten days I pay close attention to the udder as it distends with milk and an enlargement of the lacteal glands. Should the udder become hard, or "caked," several days before calving, I reduce the grain ration. However, a cow's udder can withstand an amazing amount of pressure at this time and high-producing cows are almost certain to develop "caked" quarters. No harm results if inflammation does not occur, and it is rare that pressure should be relieved by milking out the quarter. If I feel worried I call in the vet—always the prudent thing to do.

I used to get in a tremendous tizzy just before one of my cows was due to freshen, to the point of being irritated by her total unconcern with what was going on within her. Now I take the event more easily, though I am never far from the barn during the last few hours; and if indications are for calving during the night, I make a trip or two to her pen to note how matters are progressing.

Cows freshen anywhere from 270 to 290 days after conception. Heifers are likely to be earlier than mature cows. There is a widespread belief among dairymen that a heifer calf is born earlier than a bull calf, and I must admit that in general this holds true. From the 270th day on, just to be on the safe side, I check the depression at the base of the cow's tail. Also, the udder reveals a final distension that is easily recognized. Bossy is then removed from her stanchion and coaxed into the maternity ward, where a clean straw bed, hay and water await Her Highness. As a rule she is glad to get into the pen, for she is more comfortable and is delighted by the opportunity to stretch out or rub her butt against the wall. This apparently eases the pressure within.

Ordinarily a healthy cow gives birth to her calf without great difficulty and is much better left alone during the process. She dislikes being petted or fussed over. In her opinion there is no cause for excitement over a very natural occurrence. Even heifers having their first calf are far less hot and bothered than I am.

Thus far I have had only one complication. That was with Noella, my first born, about whom I hovered for days and nights after putting her in a pen well in advance, just to be on the safe side.

Action finally started while I was milking one morning. Two hoofs began to protrude as Noella grunted and heaved. I finished milking and was surprised that no more than two hoofs were visible. I hung around but noted no progress despite Noella's best squeezes and at last hurried to the house for a bite of breakfast. When I returned, the situation was unchanged. I began to worry. Something was wrong but I didn't know what. So, as usual, I rushed down the hill to Richard, hailed as "Dr. Fudd" by his wife Bea on such occasions. Dr. Fudd, also as usual, was incredibly calm over my Noella's condition. He inquired when she had started to labor, then said, "If there's no change in three hours, let me know. I've got manure to spread."

I couldn't believe anyone could be so callous, so heartless. Yet I also knew his experience of many years and innumerable bovine births and was aware that his judgment was sound. I even steeled myself to such a point that I proceeded to haul and spread manure myself, though I worked faster than ever before to get back to the barn and my pet Noella.

There was still no change, just those two hoofs in view and Noella straining hard. Again I slid down the hill through early March snow and reported to Richard. This time he returned with me. He gave one look and he said, "Those feet aren't right. They're turned up."

Not until then did I notice this unnatural position, for the calf should be born with the two front hoofs and nose appearing at about the same time, the hoofs, of course, facing down.

I was ordered to get a pail of warm water, soap and a towel. Richard washed and dried his right hand and forearm, then stuck his fist within the vulva and probed about with a most professional air. Nevertheless, he was puzzled for a moment, probed deeper and announced, "Those are hind feet. The calf's coming out wrong end first."

I failed to grasp the full meaning of such a complication. One end or the other, the job was to get the calf out.

"It's not easy," said Richard. "The hip bones are wide and it takes a lot of stretching to get them through. When the head comes first the stretching is slower and more normal."

He made a rope halter and put it on Noella's head. We led her to a big supporting post and tied her. Then Richard took another rope, tied it to the two hoofs that had emerged and gave steady pulls in rhythm with Noella's straining. Some eight inches of legs appeared. He told me to get on the rope too and both of us began to put combined weight and muscle into each heave. That was a devilish struggle. Repeatedly we pulled Noella right off her feet. She began to moan and groan, unable to strain any more. Gradually, however, those hind legs came forth until the hips were due to follow. We were now pulling with all our strength and weight, hauling with enough power to have uprooted a small tree. It seemed impossible that Noella could stand such torture.

"Now a big heave," ordered Richard, and we lay back as no two men ever did in a tug-of-war. Suddenly, like a cork from a bottle, the calf popped out. We crashed to the floor and Noella collapsed with a final moan that convinced me she was dead. I dove to her head, half-blind with sweat and tears, and found her eyes were open, her breath beginning to come in great gasps. I mumbled to her, stroked the nose and jaw that had grown from birth under my care. When she raised her head I could only gasp with relief.

Richard was occupied with the calf. "Guess the calf's dead," he said.

"The hell with the calf," I said. "I don't want Noella to die."

"She'll be all right," he replied and I took what comfort I could from such a nonchalant prediction.

But Richard was right. In a few minutes Noella

scrambled to her feet, exhausted and shaky on her legs, but otherwise sound. Soon she walked to her pen, drank gallons of warm water that I fetched, and stretched out for a long rest, poking her nose about for a calf that wasn't there and whose absence she asked about with low, plaintive cries.

Praise be that I have had only one such experience. I want no more of them. But it is striking evidence of what a healthy Holstein cow can take in the form of punishment and speedily recover.

Otherwise, the parturition phase of my dairying has been unmarred by mishap. Good health is the answer.

Penny, however, provided me with a mental case that brought variety to the barn. Penny's first calf was drowned in the drops the day before I paid for her and was to bring her home. She freshened ten days before her date and was in stanchion at the time. Loss of the calf lopped twenty-five dollars off her purchase price of two hundred, and I was satisfied since I had no intention of keeping her calf even though it was a heifer. Penny was fairly normal from then on except for a preference for her own company that kept her from mixing with the herd.

Penny had her second calf during the past winter. She was in fine condition and in the pen hours before the birth. Everything went off without a hitch. As usual, I brought gallons of warm water, wiped the calf's nose free of mucus that might hamper breathing, snipped the navel cord to a two-inch length, swabbed it with iodine and left the pen so that Penny could get on with her job of licking and drying her infant. She paid no attention to it, chewing hay instead. The calf got onto its feet and promptly went in quest of a little breakfast, nosing along Penny's flank till it reached the udder. Penny lifted a hind leg and cuffed her calf to one side. The calf was hungry and returned to the search. Again it was slapped down. I slapped Penny and told her to behave herself. The calf was not one to give up easily and soon was tottering about for the target instinct told it was not far away.

This time Penny turned and butted her offspring. Before it could get to its feet she was prodding it with her horns, not very maliciously but roughly enough to injure it. I leaped over the railing and talked to Penny. She just glowered at the calf as something she didn't want, had no interest in, and didn't wish to be bothered with. She was so adamant about it that I pushed her out of the pen and put her back in her stanchion, where she appeared quite satisfied. I thought she would begin to miss her baby and want her well-filled udder relieved of pressure by nursing.

I dried off the calf as well as I could, but the bedraggled result was far from what Mama could have done if she had tried. An hour later I carried the calf to Penny and placed its nose against a teat, whereupon it went to work with a will and more noise than seemed necessary.

Before I could catch her foot, Penny delivered a real punch that bowled the calf over in the best prize-ring style. This time she cast a really malevolent eye on her infant, and I was glad the stanchion restrained her from further attack. I carried the calf back to the pen, brought out the milking machine and removed three or four quarts from Penny's swollen udder. To this she made no objection whatever.

It is not difficult to teach a calf to drink from a pail. The pail of warm milk is held in the left hand; the first two fingers of the right hand are dipped into the milk and placed in the calf's mouth. It soon starts sucking if really hungry and follows the fingers as they move down into the pail. The calf continues to suck, the fingers are parted slightly to permit the milk to flow between them, and in a short time the calf is getting milk much faster than from a teat and displays its pleasure by a frantic wagging of its tail. Instinct prompts it to butt at the pail as it would at the udder, since this seems to make the milk flow faster; but I am now prepared for such tricks and seldom spill more than a cupful or so of milk.

For the next three days Penny's calf was fed from a pail in this manner and then, as it was a bull, I sold it. Penny never displayed the slightest desire to see her infant. I feel sure that the loss of her first calf, which she never even saw, instilled a resentment in Penny toward a natural process. The first time she had lost the satisfaction of suckling the infant; she would have none of it the second time. Maybe she will never get back to normal.

Carrying that hour-old calf to Penny reminds me of a calving during the second winter which occurred while the cow was in stanchion. My timing of the event probably was at fault. In any case, Arnold had stopped at the house, and I took him to the barn to get his opinion as to when the cow might freshen. I opened the stable door and saw the calf floundering, half in the drop, half on the floor. I ran to it and started to pick it up, regardless of filth and slime.

"Hey," called Arnold, "don't get all dirty."

He hauled me back, found an empty feed bag, noosed it about the calf's throat and strode down to the pen at the far end, the calf dragging limply behind. It seemed certain that the newborn animal would choke to death; yet when Arnold pulled it into the pen and freed it, it shook its head, snorted noisy objection to such treatment, and began the difficult job of getting four unsteady feet and legs properly braced to support it erect. Nevertheless, I have never tried to repeat the performance.

Once a calf is born and Mama is diligently applying that length of tongue, with the surface of a cheese grater, to her offspring, I leave the pair to themselves. However, I return from time to time for the elimination of the afterbirth, or placenta.

Cows are prone to eating the afterbirth, probably a protective measure dating from their wild days when all trace of a young calf had to be removed so that predatory prowlers would not know what had occurred. The afterbirth will do the cow no harm if she manages to swallow the long, fibrous mass, but there is danger that she may gag and choke to death on it. Therefore it is best to get it out of the pen as soon as it falls clear. Occasionally a cow does not lose the afterbirth, and it remains attached to the wall of the womb. Old-timers abetted nature in such instances by tying a couple of horseshoes on the end of it, the extra weight slowly pulling it free. This is hardly to be recommended since delicate membranes may be injured. Instead a veterinarian should be called. He reaches inside to "unbutton," as he terms it, the placenta. On the other hand, there are not likely to be serious complications if the afterbirth is left in the cow's body. After several days it decomposes and finally is eliminated, and a stinking mess it is. However, the prudent thing is to call the vet if the afterbirth is not dropped within twenty-four hours of the birth.

I leave Mama in the pen with her infant for twelve hours, then put her back in stanchion. Separation is easier if made at an early stage. Some dairymen part the two at once, but I prefer giving the cow some reward for the long job she has accomplished. During these twelve hours, moreover, the calf has the opportunity to get its fill of colostrum milk, a special kind of milk, thickish and dark yellow, even orange, in color, which the cow provides for two to three days, after which the milk becomes normal. This colostrum milk is high-powered stuff, loaded with nourishment, capable of destroying bacteria that may be present in the calf, and acting as a needed laxative. Obviously, the calf should get as much of it as possible to assure a good start.

Once the cow is back in stanchion, I bring the calf to her three times daily for the first three days. If I intend to keep the calf I then start teaching it to drink from a pail. If not, I sell it—to a dealer who will call when phoned or at a weekly public auction of farm products and livestock. The price is much the same either way, though I keep informed as to current market prices and know approximately what the price should be.

I keep heifer calves only from my best stock, whose milk-producing talent is proved. Thus I have yet to keep a heifer's first calf, simply because I do not know what her performance will be. After the first lactation period I have good basis for judging a heifer's ability and then can decide whether a heifer calf from her will be a reasonable gamble. For there is no guarantee that an excellent cow, bred to an outstanding sire, will produce an offspring inheriting all the best qualities of both lines. Hence, all the calves I have raised have come from the three best cows in the original herd—and I am not yet positive that they are all worth keeping—or are second calves from young stock such as Gaby and Toots.

As an experiment I may keep the first calf, if a heifer, from Gaby's daughter, Topsy. Gaby's qualities are first class, and Topsy shows every promise of equalling or improving on her dam; so the odds would not be heavy against the offspring. As I say, however, the one sure way is to wait till the end of the first lactation period, when the quantity of milk produced, the richness of the milk in butterfat and how well the animal held up in milk throughout the ten months, all will be recorded.

The heifer calf I do keep gets the best of care from the very start. For the first month she gets ten pounds of milk—twelve if she is unusually large—daily. My best hay is kept fresh in a rack in her pen from the first day. A handful of grain is put in her feedpan. It is removed if she does not eat it and another handful put in. The pen has a drinking cup with a raised platform so that she can reach the cup at an early age, but she will not need much water until her milk ration is reduced during the second month. On the sixtieth day, when she is blatting loudly for her pail, in which milk has been gradually reduced though the quantity of liquid has been maintained by adding warm water, I place the pail before her with only warm water in it. She plunges her muzzle avidly into it, takes several deep gulps and comes up with disgust on her face. Plain warm water. What a dish! From then on she loses interest in her pail and turns to the drinking cup.

After the first few days she will nibble at a wisp of hay with a comical air of "Something tells me to do this but I don't know why." She will sample the grain furtively, as though she really didn't intend to. The taste grows, the ration has to be increased, and by the end of two months she will be devouring a full ration of six to eight pounds a day.

Finally, there is a salt block on a bracket in her pen. The salt contains all of the essential trace minerals—iron, copper, magnesium, etc. And it is surprising how soon the calf will be spending considerable time licking at this block. The salt, in addition to being good for her blood, adds to her thirst so that she drinks plenty of water, which of course helps general growth.

When Richard tells me my young heifers are bigger than his—and some of them are—I find two reasons for it. He is equally generous with milk and grain, but he relies on the amount of salt in the grain mixture and waters his calves twice a day from a pail. I believe a calf needs much more salt than is contained in the grain mixture and should have water whenever she craves it.

Yet many dairymen do not provide either salt or flowing water. Some even complain that a constant supply of water makes for a messy bedding in the pen. This is true, for the calf urinates in proportion to the quantity of water drunk. I prefer the messy pen, however, particularly when my calves are so thrifty and sleek-coated that they evoke compliments. (I should add that salt blocks are installed for every two stanchions in the barn so that the cows can have as much they want. Their need for it is plain in the way the blocks diminish during the winter. Larger blocks are placed in each pasture during the summer, where one or more cows are constantly licking them. The reasoning here is extremely simple. A cow requires quantities of water to make milk. The more salt she eats, the more water she drinks and the more milk she makes, the latter, of course, up to the point of her natural ability. In addition, she gets the minerals which are necessary to her good health.)

I have abandoned feeding my calves special mixtures known as calf-starters and calf-growers. The ingredients in these feeds are not to be criticized, but they are ground very fine, especially the calf-starter, so that they can be mixed with milk or water and thus develop a taste for grain in the calf. It is this powdery texture I object to, and the calves do also. After some experimenting I settled on the same fitting ration I feed my heifers. This mixture contains all the essentials for growth, bone development and firm flesh. Moreover, it is coarse, the oats being whole, merely crushed. Young calves are eager to chew on something, and mine seem to prefer the coarse feed for this reason. Its bulk also prevents constipation, which has never bothered my calves. So they begin nosing at fitting ration when they are a few days old, suddenly acquire a liking for grain, and from then on announce their hunger for it by a great rumpus as soon as I appear with the feed pails.

Quite some time ago I read of feeding experiments at an agricultural station which disclosed that a calf does not need grain after the age of one year, granted it has grown with normal rapidity and is in excellent health. Off to a good start during the first year, the calf will continue to develop normally on a diet of hay or grass pasture. This struck me as sound. Grain, after all, is not a natural feed for bovines. Hay or grass is. Nevertheless, I was ready to admit that grains and other ingredients in a mixture could aid early growth and probably increase it beyond the nutritional content of hay. This, I reasoned, would be particularly true with the modern Holstein, which through selective breeding and special feeds has become an animal half again as large as she was thirty years ago. After the first year, however, with the big bone framework well under way, hay should be able to take over and continue the building job; for roughage means bulk, and a bulky feed develops the big barrel a good milking cow must have.

Thus far the results in my herd have been entirely in favor of the experiment. None of the young stock I have raised, from Noella on, has had grain after the first birthday until a couple of months before she calved. And every one has all the size her ancestry would warrant. Noella, in fact, is taller and longer than her mother. Raki is taller than her mother, but has not yet filled out as Noella has. Blondy is taller than her mother. Vicky is as big as her mother, whereas Bonnie, her half-sister, is oversize for her age. The others are too young for comparison, though their present size gives every indication that they will equal and probably surpass their mothers.

I have tried to argue the matter with other dairymen whom I know to be generous feeders. But they are hard to convince, though they admit my young stock is every bit as thrifty as their own. I point out that an important economic factor is involved; for grain feeds are not cheap, and if they can be dispensed with for a period of a year or more, the saving is considerable. They still shake their heads in opposition.

In my opinion their very generosity with feed is the barrier. They are so accustomed to feeding amply, preferring to overfeed rather than underfeed, that they no longer will accept a cheaper diet, which they consider poor economy. Naturally no harm is done to the growing animal by graining it throughout the second year, though I have seen some that were plain fat, and fat on a cow does not make milk. But to a large degree the grain, I now believe, is wasted during the second year.

Anyway, my heifers will continue to get six to eight pounds of grain daily until they are a year old; then they must be satisfied with an abundance of hay. And they certainly are, judging from the speed with which they put it away.

I should add that yearlings during the winter get a small amount of beet pulp, but that is more for variety than actual nourishment.

My heifers have plenty of size and weight at the age of fifteen months, when most dairymen breed them; but, as I have said, I wait until they are eighteen months old, regardless of their physical stature. They are not, of course, fully grown at fifteen months, or eighteen, and I think it better to allow as much time as possible for uninterrupted growth, with all the bodily functions concentrating on that single aim rather than being divided between growth and the development of the foetus.

Here, however, is an economic factor which a dairyman must consider if he looks upon cows from the strictly business viewpoint. Heifers, in his opinion, must start producing milk as early as possible; and from then on his goal is to extract as much milk, or profit, from them as he can. That attitude is absolutely sound, if he is a good herdsman and his animals are well fed and well cared for, because that is the way to obtain maximum milk. If a cow is pushed to her capacity so that she is finished at the age of eight years, he gets rid of her as no longer profitable. He has no time or desire to treat cows as pets, to be satisfied with a little less milk and so keep them around for as long as possible.

Cows, however, happen to appeal to me in that way. I don't regard my dairying as a business, but merely as a satisfying method of paying my bills in addition to which I have the companionship and affection of my animals. Having raised a calf to milk-producing age, I want to keep her around as long as she gives enough milk to pay her keep. Nor do I want more cows than I can manage in just that way. So I breed my heifers three months later than the business dairyman, I get all the milk I can from them without pushing them, and some day I probably will have several ancient dams hanging about the farm that I simply can't force myself to part with. They won't add much to my monetary wealth, but they will still respond to a pat or a caress.

But to get back to the breeding.

All my breeding is accomplished by artificial insemination, one of two modern innovations in dairying which made the project feasible when I first became owner of a small herd and wondered what to do with the animals; the other being, of course, machine milking. Bulls scare me as no other animal can that I have encountered, wild or tame. They are fearsome brutes with murder in their sullen eyes. I wouldn't have one on the farm as a gift. Their vicious streak is never far below the surface; and when it gains control, as it certainly will some day, a goring is almost the inevitable outcome. All the pleasure of dairying would vanish if I had a bull to manage. Moreover, I could not afford the price of a good bull and obviously a scrub bull will contribute nothing to herd improvement. Another argument against the bull is that in a small herd his feeding and care is a sizable item when compared with value received.

As for artificial insemination, I cannot discover a sound argument against it provided the organization is efficiently directed and the service is reliable. The breeding co-operative that I belong to can boast of both these achievements. It has expanded rapidly just since my arrival in these parts; new bulls are constantly being searched out and purchased for the four major breeds—Holstein, Guernsey, Ayrshire and Jersey—and the management has been so capable that an annual refund of some twenty per cent is paid on insemination fees. In other words, for approximately fifty dollars a year, my cows are bred to superior bulls, rated as "proven" by the performance records of their daughters. Yet it would cost me about one hundred and fifty dollars just to feed my own bull, in addition to the extra work and ever-present hazard involved.

For the modest fee of five dollars I obtain service for one of my cows from a purebred bull worth thousands of dollars. A telephone call before ten A.M. brings the inseminator the same day, either the very morning or in the afternoon, according to my judgment. I have a choice of three or four bulls for every day in the week, and their records are available to aid my selection—a point of special interest to me at present since I am breeding for a higher butterfat content rather than increased milk. The man works with dispatch since the cow to be bred has been kept in a stanchion. He uses disinfectants on his hands, even on his boots, and wears rubber gloves. In five minutes the job is accomplished, and a paper form filled out for my own records. Three services are included in the five-dollar fee. If conception does not occur, a fee of two dollars is charged for each service thereafter, though if a cow fails to conceive with the fifth service she probably has a congenital weakness and may have to be disposed of. That is for the veterinarian to decide. Inbreeding is avoided—a common cause of herd deterioration when one bull runs with the cows —by noting the sire of a heifer being bred for the first time and thereafter.

No, I'll take artificial insemination. It is the happy answer to the small dairyman's prayer. Then I can visit the hulking beasts that sire my young ones and thumb my nose at them as they glower and paw dirt in the air, only a few feet away—but behind heavily charged electric fencing.

The big problem in breeding is to assure conception, and this holds true when a bull runs with the herd as well as with artificial insemination. In fact, the two methods are about even on the percentage of pregnancies from first services. The time element is the controlling factor, and this is where a herdsman's observation and judgment can go far toward assuring conception with first service.

The cow comes into heat about every twenty-one

days, the range being from eighteen to twenty-four. The length of the heat period varies from six to thirty-six hours, the average being fifteen hours. The cow, being a lazy individual, does not release her egg for future fertilization until some twelve hours *after* the heat period *ends*. The sperm requires from four to six hours to navigate the long canal to the ovary. The egg will live about eight hours unfertilized. The sperm will live about twelve hours in the cow's reproductive tract.

Thus both variable and constant timings are to be calculated when one summons the inseminator. For example, it is almost impossible to tell just when the heat period starts, because one cannot be with the cows day and night. I figure that ten to twelve hours remain of the heat period from the time I notice the cow is in heat, and hope for the best. The usual recommendation is that a cow observed in heat early in the morning should be bred that afternoon or, if in heat in the afternoon, the following morning.

Obviously the inseminator cannot schedule his call at a fixed hour. With many other herds to visit he cannot do more than arrive during the morning or during the afternoon. This introduces another variable time element which seems to complicate the problem so much that it is a near miracle that a cow ever gets bred. Yet statistics show that some seventy-five per cent of cows bred conceive on the first service. The best safeguard amid a number of uncertainties, according to my observation, is to be late rather than early in having a cow bred. Even if a cow is bred twelve hours after the heat period ends—which is also the time when the egg is released—the sperm can still reach the egg in six hours, or an hour or so before the egg dies unfertilized. But if a cow is bred before the heat period ends, the sperm will reach its destination well in advance of the egg and may die before the egg arrives.

As a result, I don't rush for a telephone the moment I find a cow in heat. Noting a cow in heat in late afternoon, I have on several occasions held her until the following afternoon, instead of the recommended following morning, and conception has resulted. Similarly, a cow observed in heat in late morning is held until the following morning. In both instances approximately twenty-four hours intervene between the noting of the heat period and the time of insemination. Following this practice, I have had extremely few repeats, or second or third services.

On the other hand I take as many precautions as possible. After a cow freshens I watch carefully for her first heat period. She may bawl loudly for release from her stanchion, or she may be merely fidgety or even unexpectedly affectionate—signs which are recognized after close association with the herd. When at liberty with the rest of the herd, she will try to mount the others. They refuse, but in turn will mount her and she will accept. During the winter I may suspect a cow of being in heat at a time when it would be difficult to turn out the herd. In that event I release my suspected one so that she can wander up and down the floor. If she is in heat she will try to mount one of the stanchioned cows.

I mark the date on a large calendar in the barn and in the house. Then I mark the date three weeks later and the one six weeks later along with the cow's name. Just before her second heat period should occur, I again pay close attention to her and usually detect indications I might otherwise have overlooked. With this date as a check, I am fairly sure of her third and fourth heat, at which time I have her bred. Once she is bred, I mark her name on dates another three and six weeks away. On these dates I again watch her, for if she has not conceived she will come into heat and have to be bred a second time. This becomes so mechanical that it is no bother whatever. Every morning while I have breakfast I cast an eye at the calendar on the wall; and if a name is written for that day, I keep it in mind until I am satisfied the cow is or is not in heat.

For breeding is one of the most important phases of dairying and, since Nature has made it just about as uncertain as she can, special care is essential. I may be occasionally slipshod about some herd duties but not with breeding. It is the key to profitable dairying.

To produce her best milk a cow should be in milk for ten months, then dry for two months, and at the end of each year drop a calf. Then she starts all over again. A cow bred three months or more after she calves, instead of from six to eight weeks afterward, is called upon to give milk for a longer period than is good for her. The result is that either the milk yield becomes so small that it is of little value or she goes dry of her own accord. One way or the other, an interval occurs when she is a "boarder" and not paying for her keep.

In recent years many dairymen have been breeding for fall and early-winter calving rather than following the old-fashioned and more natural schedule of spring calving. Milk is most plentiful and, of course, cheapest in late spring and early summer, the months of May,

June and July, because of both spring freshening and the flush period resulting from early green pasture. By contrast, milk is least plentiful in late fall and early winter, and so brings the highest prices of the year to the producer. The higher price for milk is partly offset by the increased cost of feed when cows are indoors, but this difference may be regained in the spring when a cow which has freshened during the winter shows a second upward trend in milk production because of young grass pasture. If one breeds a spring cow six or eight weeks after she calves, a month or more can be gained each year so that after three years she should be calving in January instead of May. However, a cow calving in late July or August might better be held an extra month or so for breeding to delay her freshening date until September or later. With my herd, calving is rather evenly spread through the winter months. This is fairly satisfactory, but it will be more satisfactory when I have moved back several spring cows to a midwinter schedule.

I have said that in my breeding I am now selecting bulls whose daughters' records show good milk production, but also an increase in butterfat over their dams. My aim here is to increase profit without forcing a cow to produce extra milk. I sell my milk to one of the two largest dairy corporations in the east, which ships mainly to New York City from this and other areas in the New York milkshed. The price paid to me is based on a complicated formula and can vary according to the butterfat content of each dairyman's milk. A butterfat percentage of 3.5 is rated normal. For every tenth of a point below that mean, a deduction in price of five to six cents per hundredweight of milk is made. Thus milk with a butterfat percentage of 3.2 would be three points down, and the price would be fifteen to eighteen cents lower. This does not appear as a very appreciable sum, yet on a daily average of three hundredweight the difference is about fifty cents, which over a year means more than one hundred and fifty dollars.

On the other hand, milk with a butterfat percentage in excess of 3.5 brings a premium of five to six cents per hundredweight, so that the price for 3.8 milk is fifteen to eighteen cents higher than the formula price, or some one hundred and fifty dollars' additional profit for a daily average of three hundredweight.

An increase in butterfat percentage is gained almost entirely through breeding. Some bulls and cows show a high test, others do not. Feed, from all I can learn on a subject that is still far from understood, is secondary. The Holstein cow is the champion milk producer of all breeds, but her butterfat test averages the lowest. The range is from 2.8 or even lower to a full 4.0 for some purebreds. Evidently, a 2.8 cow may produce a lot of milk, but the price for her milk is thirty-five to forty cents less per hundredweight, which represents a serious loss over several years.

My herd test averages 3.5 or perhaps a shade higher. I would like to raise it to 3.7, the maximum I could expect from good grade Holsteins. The financial return therefrom would permit me to economize on purchased grain in that I would not need to feed heavily to increase each cow's milk production. I could be satisfied with a good steady yield and not be tempted to overtax her productive ability in order to augment the milk check, a practice that inevitably weakens the cow.

CHAPTER 12

THUS FAR MY HERD HAS BEEN REASONABLY free of the various bovine maladies. Perhaps I should knock on wood, but I am not convinced that luck has played a great part in this. My cows are maintained in good health and a healthy cow, especially the rugged Holstein, just isn't subject to disease. Hence, my own experience in this phase of dairying has been rather limited, and far more learned discussions of the various ailments can be found in books or pamphlets written by professionals. In the early days I called a veterinarian or consulted with Richard when something went amiss. I still do, because a good vet can diagnose and prescribe for an illness far better than I ever will be able to. To me he represents cheap insurance.

I have avoided bloat to date by introducing my cows to spring pasture on a gradual basis: an hour for the first day or two, when the dew is gone, two hours for a couple of days, then a whole morning, finally the entire day and night. Before being turned out each day they are fed a full ration of hay and grain. Within a week their digestive systems are adjusted to the new diet of succulent grass and the danger of bloat is pretty well eliminated. When autumn frosts arrive the animals are strictly barred from any legume browsing, particularly alfalfa.

Scours, or diarrhea, has never bothered my calves, but every spring, before the herd is put on pasture, at least some of my cows get mild cases of it. This is caused apparently by the drinking water, which even in a spring or deep well is temporarily adulterated by the excessive surface water which results from thawing snow and ice and rain.

If scours becomes acute I dose the animal according to the vet's instructions; but never having had an abiding faith in medicines, I am inclined to let the cow recover through her own healthy resistance—a process which takes three or four days. The milk yield may drop at such times, but except in severe cases it returns to normal.

Scours is believed to be contagious, capable of being transmitted from one barn to another, particularly on footgear. Unaware of this, I was distinctly, though temporarily, shocked to be hustled out of Richard's barn one morning when I blandly announced that some of my cows had scours.

Chapped teats have not bothered my cows to any great extent because I do not apply a warm, wet towel to their udders prior to milking to stimulate the milk flow. In winter wet or damp teats are almost certain to become chapped, and when this occurs, machine milking becomes difficult, if not painful. Instead, I massage the udder lightly with my dry hands, then squirt a bit of milk from each teat into a stripping cup—so named because it is used to "strip" or milk out the last drops of milk which the machine may have missed. Expert handling of the machine, however, almost eliminates the need for stripping.

Mastitis is the real bugbear of all dairymen. It is an infection of the udder resulting in thick, stringy milk which must not be sold for human consumption. Millions of pounds of milk are lost annually through this disease and as yet there is no certain permanent cure. Nevertheless, considerable progress toward this end has been made with penicillin and other mold products.

Mastitis results from a number of causes such as a bruised udder, an injured teat, cold from drafts or lying on bare concrete, unsanitary conditions in the barn, careless manipulation of the milking machine, too much grain, or too rich a grain mixture. High-producing cows are much more liable to mastitis than their less generous sisters since their udders are weakened by being pushed to capacity yield.

My original herd included several chronic mastitis cases when I took over, the result mainly of overfeeding to increase the milk yield.

Penicillin in its present ointment form was not in use when I called the vet to treat my first patient. The doc, however, was not the kind to baby his clients.

"Don't spend your money on me," he said. "You can do it just as well as I can."

So he sold me a 40 cc. syringe with needle and a vial of 20 cc. of penicillin in a saline solution. He told me to sterilize the needle in boiling water, put 200 cc. of sterile water in a bottle, add 5 cc. of penicillin solution, fill the syringe, insert the needle in the milk canal of the infected teat and push the plunger. I was to repeat the treatment until all 205 cc. had been used.

"It's easy," he said. "And I'm busy." With that he drove off.

I have a strong aversion to work of this nature. I worry about doing something wrong, about hurting the animal. I am beset with visions of the needle stabbing through the whole teat, of a kick by the cow that drives the needle deep into her udder. Yet I had been left alone and the cow had to be treated. I got firmly seated on a milkstool, surrounded by my medical paraphernalia, and set to work with hands that were not too steady.

Fortunately, the cow was very patient. I suspect she had been treated for mastitis on many previous occasions and so did not object. Anyway, despite clumsiness and nervousness, I managed to get every drop of the stuff inside the affected quarter.

One cow later proved too fidgety for my ministrations. She didn't kick hard, but her foot cuffed my hand just enough to knock it away every time I was about to insert the needle. Again I conferred with the vet. This time he sold me a bull lead.

A bull lead is a miniature ice tongs with metal balls instead of points on the two tips. The balls are inserted in the cow's nostrils, where they grip securely on the slightest pull; the harder the pull, the firmer they hold. The cow's head then is hauled up and the rope on the bull lead is tied to the top of the stanchion. The reasoning behind all this is that the cow is so perturbed by having her head hoisted on high that she pays no attention to what is taking place in other regions.

The reasoning proved sound. My jumpy cow braced herself solidly on all four feet and apparently wouldn't have quivered if I had built a fire beneath her. I proceeded with my injections; and, when I released the tongs from her nose, she shook her head in amazed relief that nothing had hurt her.

Treatment is much easier at present, however. The remedy is contained in a small tube, like a sample of toothpaste. The long tip of the tube is protected by a screw cap until ready for use. The tip is then inserted into the teat opening, and the ointment is squeezed into the canal. A gentle massage spreads the ointment throughout the infected quarter, where it is left for twenty-four hours. The quarter is then milked out and, as a rule, the infection disappears in another twenty-four hours. But it probably will return.

Nevertheless, I am not greatly bothered by mastitis now that I am rid of all but two of the original herd and the rest of my milkers are young and carefully handled.

Stepped-on teats are the one hazard that good management cannot prevent. In getting up, a cow will occasionally place one hind hoof on a teat just as she heaves up her rear. The result may be a bruised and swollen teat or one with a nasty gash in it, almost severing the tip. Mastitis follows, usually accompanied by severe inflammation and fever. Treatment is difficult—a case for the vet; unquestionably.

Too generous feeding, which forces a cow to produce milk to peak capacity or beyond, is likely to bring on mastitis, the bug or bugs apparently being in the udder but held under control by the cow's resistance until a weakness develops and permits the bug to gain dominance. This is one of the main reasons why I feed lightly rather than heavily. Instead of following the accepted formula for Holsteins of one pound of grain for every three pounds of milk, I feed one pound for every four pounds of milk during the winter, and one pound for every six to seven pounds when the cows are on good pasture. This is economy where economy is important—the feed bill—and I am sure it helps to keep mastitis to a minimum in my herd. I may get a bit less milk from a cow—though anyone should be satisfied with an average of thirty-five pounds daily for ten months from a cow like Gaby—but in the end I make it up in the lowered feed bill and the very reduced loss of milk because of mastitis.

One other way to keep mastitis under control lies in the correct handling of the milking machine.

The machine operates from a vacuum pipe over the stanchions with a stallcock for every two cows, the vacuum being created by a motor-driven pump. All of the several types of machines have a heavy metal "head" fitting tightly to the opening of the pail receiving the milk. To this head are attached four "cups," consisting of a metal shell in which is inserted a rubber "inflation." A rubber tube from the shell sucks air out between shell and inflation, causing the latter to collapse against the teat with sufficient pressure to force milk into it. The milk is then carried to the pail by another rubber tube.

Most modern machines also have a pulsator in the head which makes the inflations work alternately instead of all at once, thus approximating hand milking. My type of machine also has the pail, with its head, slung beneath the cow on a surcingle, in contrast with others which place the pail to one side of the cow. The advantage here is that the cow cannot kick the pail. Also, when the pail is hung on the surcingle, the pulsing motion causes the pail to sway slightly, the sway helping to extract the milk. In fact, the weight of the pail can be adjusted, by the surcingle, so that greater forward and downward pressure can be exerted on teats which are slow to milk. With the stationary-pail type, on the other hand, some farmers are obliged to hang horseshoes or weights on the long rubber tubes between teats and pail to obtain the extra pressure.

The suction in an inflation is surprisingly strong, as one can test by inserting a thumb into it. This pressure must be controlled by a gauge registering the pull and a release valve which must be adjusted to prevent pressure rising above about twelve pounds. Close attention to this point is essential, for teats and udder can be injured when the pull is too strong. Once the valve is regulated, the gauge should be checked constantly to make sure the pressure is right.

Because of this strong pull, moreover, the inflation must not remain on a teat for a long period. This, of course, is largely up to the cow. If she lets her milk down quickly, she can be milked in three or four minutes. If she does not, or if her teats are abnormally muscular, or if the sphincter muscles are abnormally tight, the milking operation is necessarily longer.

Six minutes is about the maximum to avoid injury. A cow taking longer than that to milk out is almost certain to develop a weakness that leads to mastitis.

Little can be done to induce an old cow with bad milking habits to change them. Warm wet towels applied to the udder just before milking or massaging with the hands will help some, but the cow is the one that has control. For this reason, I take extra pains with my first-calf heifers in an endeavor to start them off right for machine milking. I am extra patient with them during the first several weeks when they tend to object to the pressure, even the appearance, of the machine. I do everything in my power to allay nervousness or fear, talk to them and pat them, for only a fully relaxed animal can let down her milk rapidly and be milked dry by machine—which is important in itself.

After I have massaged the cow's udder lightly and started the flow of milk from each teat, I allow approximately one minute—never more than a minute and a half —to pass before attaching the machine. Experimentation has shown that this initial stimulation to letting down milk is passed to the cow's brain by her nervous system, whence the order is transmitted to the lacteal glands in the cow's udder—a bit of telegraphing requiring about one minute. If the machine is attached too soon, the inflations work on empty teats, and this can be harmful. If it is attached too late, the stimulating impulse has died and empty or half-filled teats result.

When properly trained, however, the cow begins to let down her milk as soon as the machine appears. I have several cows on whom I now attach the machine immediately after squeezing a few drops of milk from each teat, and the full flow of milk is immediate. Two other cows are always the first to be milked because they start to let down their milk the moment they hear the pump start. If I compel them to wait, they drip up to a quart of milk onto the platform and the glands tighten so that the operation takes much longer.

A third point to be watched is the speed of the pulsator, which can be regulated by a set screw. At first I set this speed at what I thought compared with hand milking, but I discovered it was much too fast. Now I have slowed it down to about forty-five pulsations per minute. This seemed at first to be intolerably slow but is actually easier on the cow and results in faster milking. The prolonged, steady pull of the inflation extracts a full stream of milk, all that the teat can hold and more, whereas the faster, shorter beat cuts the stream when the teat is only a half or even a third empty. This abrupt, unnatural halting of the milk flow is irritating to the cow and can lead to trouble.

Handled properly, the milking machine is easier on the cow than all but the most expert hand milking. It also saves time, is more sanitary and—something I appreciate—affords spare minutes while it functions either to sit on a milkstool or perform minor duties such as mixing beet pulp, spreading bedding, or inspecting the calves.

I have always liked good applejack and in France frequently chose its Gallic counterpart, *calvados*, to finish off a sumptuous dinner. Now I find my cows have a similar taste. One of them might even be called a lush when early autumn frosts and winds knock apples from trees and the still warm sun produces fermentation in the bruised fruit.

Penny is my alcoholic ungulate. She went on one gorgeous binge, survived a weekend which is eternally lost to her blanked-out brain, and came to with a hangover of gargantuan proportions. In fact she very nearly passed out for good. So now I regard the local apple-jack supply with baneful eye and am elated when the wind topples over old appletrees bordering my meadows, so old and neglected that they produced only nubbins unworthy of poor cider.

I missed Penny from the herd one morning when I brought the cows to the barn. She frequently wandered off by herself and then, realizing her companions had departed, would stroll in a few minutes later. So I proceeded with milking, expecting to see her at the door. She had not appeared when milking was finished, and I turned out the others and went looking for her. I finally found Penny slumped among bushes in a far corner. She hardly budged when I prodded her. I noticed her eyes had a glassy stare and passed my hand before them. Not a blink. I also noticed appleseeds in her droppings nearby and knew she had been eating apples, but I could not believe that an animal could get blind drunk. Unable to get her on her feet and genuinely alarmed, I summoned the doc.

When he arrived the two of us managed to stand Penny up and head her for the barn. The spectacle had its comical side, for Penny would stagger off at a tangent exactly like Leon Errol in his best moments in the old Follies. Gaining some balance she would move ahead for a few steps, then slither off in the other direction. I laughed until I noticed Doc was not at all amused.

"She's bad," he said. "She may die. Almost complete paralysis."

That sobered me, though it had no effect on the teetery Penny. We got her to the barn and tucked her head in a stanchion she couldn't see. She collapsed.

"Black coffee's best," said Doc. "Plenty strong and black. Dissolve these tablets in it, get a quart or more of it down her and keep at it every hour till she comes out of it . . . If she does," he added ominously.

As usual, the doc departed on other business. I drove in a hurry to the nearest store, bought several pounds of cheap ground coffee and prepared an initial dose strong enough and black enough to satisfy a coffee fiend. I filled a long-necked bottle and, while I held Penny's head up and her mouth open with one arm and hand, shoved the bottle opening to the base of her tongue. As I tilted it I tried to get her to swallow; otherwise she might breathe the liquid into her lungs.

It was a long struggle. She had just strength enough to pull free of the bottle again and again. I got drenched with black coffee, and so did she, but some of it reached her belly. I stayed on the job all day. The glaze left her eyes; she got to her feet and even nibbled at some hay. For two days her actions indicated that she had a horrible headache, but eventually she got back to normal. Except for milk. Her milk yield dropped almost to zero and never did recover fully for the remainder of that lactation period.

I now make sure that apples never accumulate on the ground in any quantity where the cows can get at them.

The only other disease with which I am acquainted—and that indirectly, I am glad to say—is Bang's disease, or contagious abortion. Tuberculosis once was the dread affliction of cows, but it has been reduced to negligible proportion, less than one per cent of all the cows in the country being tubercular. Bang's disease can be even more destructive, but progress is being made to combat it. It brings on abortion, well before the date of freshening, and an infected cow will pass the disease throughout the herd, which then can only be disposed of as beef.

No absolute cure has yet been found for Bang's disease. Prevention, however, now appears assured through vaccination. All my calves are vaccinated at the age of six months. Once a year every animal over eighteen months gets a blood test, blood samples being drawn by the vet and tested by the Animal Industry Division of the State Department of Agriculture. My herd having reacted negative to three successive tests, it is now qualified as accredited—free, that is, of Bang's disease. I prize the shiny gold seal on the paper declaring the status of my herd. It is the best guarantee available against contagious abortion. Moreover, it adds to the value of my stock in the event that I should sell an animal as a milking cow. Accompanying her would be a health chart issued by the State showing that she had been vaccinated and blood-tested as negative.

This health chart should be exacted by anyone purchasing milking cows. It is a vital safeguard for the future of the herd.

There are other points to consider in establishing a herd of milking cows, and the inexperienced person would do well to locate a reputable dairyman in the locality who is a good judge of cows, hears of one or more animals being offered for sale, and has a general knowledge of the management of farms in the vicinity. His fee will not be excessive—probably a fixed amount for every animal bought; and in the end he will save time and money for the purchaser, who should succeed by this means in assembling a herd whose individual performances are sufficiently known to assure good results.

In addition to demanding a health chart for each cow, a purchaser should try to buy from herds belonging to the Dairy Herd Improvement Association. Field men from D.H.I.A. call once a month at each member farm. They stay the night to take milk samples from each cow at night and in the morning, test the milk for butterfat, weigh the total milk yield per cow for two milkings, record the amount of grain, silage and hay fed and the value of milk, and finally arrive at the cash profit or loss deriving from each cow. When such records are available, the purchaser knows exactly what kind of animal he is acquiring. Such cows, when good performers, will cost more, but the gamble is reduced to a minimum.

Livestock dealers are numerous in dairy country, but their offerings should be closely inspected by an expert. A health chart, moreover, may be valueless if the cow has been in contact with other animals that might have been exposed to Bang's disease. Dealers are businessmen; they handle cows in numbers and cannot take the precautions possible for an individual farmer. Also their profit is about the same from a poor cow as a good one.

Dairy farmers occasionally sell one or several head of stock. Here again care should be exercised. Obviously, the farmer is not selling his finest stock. Only a good judge of cows can say with fair assurance, in the absence of actual records, that a certain animal is worth the price asked.

A good place to acquire cows is the public sales, where farmers, obliged to quit dairying for one reason or another, offer at auction their livestock, machinery, even furniture, house and land. Such sales are announced in advance in the local newspaper. These auctions are worth attending for entertainment alone, but they also are reasonable guarantees against misrepresentation. If the stock being sold is accredited and supplied with health charts, the fact will be widely heralded. The animals, also, are in the barn for inspection, where they can be tested for mastitis. A good herdsman can judge their size, type, age and gentleness at his leisure, and the opinions of other observers quick to note faults and shortcomings are outspoken.

Auctioneers, moreover, must maintain their reputation, for they belong to the community and must deal again and again with the same people. They prefer to admit defects in a cow rather than be caught in deception. If not entirely satisfied, the prospective purchaser can ask frankly whether an animal is "square and right," the customary phrase to signify that she milks properly from all four quarters and that each quarter is normal. The auctioneer will hardly dare to reply untruthfully.

Buying a cow in these circumstances is like buying a hat. If size, type and quality are not what the salesman represents, the hat, or the cow, can be returned. The gamble is not entirely eliminated, but it is reduced to as narrow a margin as can be expected. One other point in favor of these public sales is that occasionally the crowd is small or lacking in enthusiasm, the auctioneer is unable to arouse a bidding spirit, and first-rate cows can be bought at advantageous prices. They must be sold, then and there, at the best price offered and, if bidding is weak, the unlucky farmer disposing of his stock is the one to suffer.

Such sales have a holiday flavor. At least half the farmers present have no intention of buying, but they will postpone all but the most urgent tasks to join the gathering, gossip, guffaw at the earthy humor of the auctioneer, and finally go home with a store of small talk that will last for many an evening.

Here also a lot of dairy terminology became clear to me. I soon discovered that a cow described as "fresh" was not necessarily impudent. It meant that Bossy had very recently dropped a calf.

"She's springin'" was a term that mystified me for some time. Since the cow in question was stock-still, by deduction I rejected any idea of leaping motion. Yet my unschooled eye failed to discern something that was plain to every farmer. Later I learned the phrase meant that the cow's udder was getting large with milk as calving time approached.

The first time a neighbor pointed to a cow and said to me, "She's gone Sweeney" I could only stare from him to the cow, utterly baffled. The remark seemed so far-fetched that I didn't mind demanding an explanation. He laughed and indicated her shoulders. Then I noticed how her shoulder bones stuck out from her body at an abnormal angle, almost as though they were out of joint. The condition develops from weakness in the tendons and joints and detracts seriously from the animal's appearance. As for the origin of the term, no one thus far has been able to inform me who the original Sweeney was and what he looked like.

"Flash" was not difficult to comprehend. It is never

used in the negative; and when a good dairyman says, "She has flash," there can be no misconception, for the cow is patently superior in every line and aspect, with all the alertness a healthy dairy cow displays in her very quiet way.

Since an "open" heifer quite logically would be one not yet bred, the conclusion followed that a "close" heifer was one that had been bred.

"Handling" was not so easy. In fact, I have garnered two definitions for the term. A "handling" cow is one handling the calf within her or handling the calf already born and beside her. I leave the term to other rural philologists.

Of them all I still prefer "in good rig." It recalls the clipper ship under full sail in a sparkling blue sea, a smart and shiny buggy dashing along a dusty country road, or an urban dandy promenading Main Street or Fifth Avenue. To me now, however, it means handsome black and white Holsteins against a background of deep, green grass.

CHAPTER 13

ONE OF THE MAJOR SOURCES OF DISCONTENT for the city person turning farmer, according to my solicitous friends, is monotony, the monotony of solitude, of dull routine. I admitted the validity of the assertion, in that the sharp change from crowded, noisy streets to quiet lanes demanded long consideration and a great deal of introspection. At the same time I flouted the contention that monotony could not be circumvented. I was eager to experiment with solitude, and I had figured out a yearly work schedule for subsistence farming that promised both variety and leisure.

Overnight, my farming horizon was cluttered with cows. I was a neophyte dairyman. Immediately I was snared in a routine that I had never contemplated and that was far more exacting than the fairly elastic regime of subsistence farming. With the latter it is possible to sleep late if that desire happens to become overpowering, or to gossip with neighbors right up to suppertime. Dairying permits no such liberties with the clock. The man who first said, "Dairying means being chained to a cow," summed up the situation with commendable terseness.

Viewed from its most unalluring side, the side that should be closely examined by anyone considering dairying as a livelihood, it exacts work, time and thought for three hundred and sixty-five days a year. There is never a day off, never a holiday; Sundays offer the same schedule as every week day. There is never an opportunity to sleep late. Three times a day there are chores that can never be postponed—two daily milkings and cleaning the barn. It is an unyielding chain whose every link may get roundly and periodically cursed but remains just as intact as ever, a relentless shackle between dairyman and cows.

However, to turn away in dismay because of that inauspicious introduction would mean missing all the brighter phases of dairying. For example, dairying affords more intermittent leisure during the daily routine than other kinds of farming. The work, when properly organized, is not too arduous for any healthy person. Even during the strenuous haying season, time off is made obligatory by the weather, whose showers drive me to a comfortable chair where I relax though some well-cured hay is getting wet, for I have come to expect a certain amount of that kind of bad luck. And there are the responsive cows, the promising heifers, the zany, ever-amusing calves.

I find the balance between work and play during an average day at High Meadows just about perfect. Moreover, with a certain amount of experience behind me, a major incident is required to disturb that balance.

A typical winter day for me holds with surprising regularity to the following pattern.

I arise at five o'clock every morning throughout the year. That is earlier than necessary, but I have a strong dislike for rushing abruptly into work of any kind. My spirit and stamina are greatly bolstered if I can have a few minutes of repose to contemplate the job ahead, remind myself of things to be done beyond the customary routine, and finally start forth with everything under control. So I brew a pot of tea while I wash and shave. I may be the only farmer in the region who shaves every day but it is an old habit. I feel better throughout the day if I have shaved, so I continue to ply the razor every morning, regardless of caustic remarks from my neighbors. With face smooth, I have a half-hour before going to the barn at 5:45.

My neighbors show no timidity in declaring this half-hour a silly waste of time that might better be spent in bed. I don't argue with them. Let them sleep to the last minute, then hurry to the barn and plunge almost breathlessly into chores. To me it is one of the pleasantest times of a pleasant day. I sit in a big armchair in the warm living room, drink two glasses of tea, and smoke a couple of cigarettes. Once the milking job has been reviewed, my thoughts can wander as they please. The house is wonderfully quiet, unless the north wind is howling; silence is profound over the countryside. There is nothing to disturb me in my wrapping of tranquillity.

Exactly at 5:45 I climb into gum boots, don whatever

extra garments the temperature outside demands, and stroll to the barn through black night if there is no snow on the ground or the glowing dark that accompanies a blanket of snow. The barn door may be frozen in its groove; but a crowbar is permanently handy, the door is quickly loosened and I am inside, feeling the first warmth from the horse stalls, which are separated by a partition from the cow barn. The horses greet me with a nickering that means "hurry with the grain." Molly bangs one foot against her manger to spur me on. Once Molly and Doc are munching oats, I measure grain for the cows and am off to the really warm air of the cow barn.

The cows have been shifting noisily since the lights went on. Now they gaze at me, wondering why I am so slow; the younger ones bawl in a basso profundo that contrasts strongly with their size.

One glance of inspection and I am assured that all has been quiet during the night. Then I go to the feed alley with beet pulp, and the commotion rises to a new pitch. Heads bob up and down, and long tongues reach out for the feed basket. While I spill out a ration for one cow, her neighbor develops near-hysteria at the tantalizing sight. I talk to the animals, joke with them, but this is no time for ear-scratching. "Bring on the grain" is the bovine cry. And such an uproar when they get the first whiff of the mixed grain.

Yet I can't go as fast as I, or they, would like because the amount of grain varies with each cow, according to the amount of milk she is giving. Some have left their beet pulp untouched, waiting for the grain to be placed neatly on top, like frosting on cake. Then they really go to work, and what a chomping and slavering and rumbling there is once they all are served. I am delighted to have guests at the house who appreciate a good dinner, but never have I been rewarded with such gustatory zeal as my cows provide. A whole day of toil is reimbursed by those few moments.

Next I go to the milkhouse where I assemble the milking machine, warm it with hot water, and gather up my pails. Back with the cows, I find that milking proceeds rapidly, yet at the same time allows me occasional minutes to rearrange bedding, spread a forkful here and there, play with the calves, pet the cats, admire new kittens while their mother closes her eyes in rapturous self-commendation, or fill and light a pipe. In about an hour the milking is ended, utensils are taken to the milkhouse, filled cans are set out for the truck.

Up in the mows, I hurriedly fork hay down the chute, for the mows are iron cold and my fingertips begin to burn through my leather gloves. Back in the barn, I spread the hay to the waiting cows, many of whom have lain down as soon as milking was over. They stay in that position, happy to have their heads buried in hay which they can devour in mouthfuls with no effort except that of chewing and swallowing.

I respond to the clamor from the horse stalls by stuffing their mangers with hay.

And again I am back in the milkhouse. There I scrub the utensils, swab them in steaming water, rinse them and place them on racks to drain. At this point I pause and light a cigarette before heading for the house, the breakfast menu completely outlined in my mind.

Just two hours have passed. It is quarter to eight, and

I am in time for the news and the weather forecast on the radio. As I listen to it, I get breakfast started in the kitchen. Dawn is beginning to creep through the windows.

Breakfast is an occasion with me. I have never been of the toast-bacon-coffee school, but seek instead as much variety as possible in this initial repast of the day. And now that I am farming, with two hours of work accomplished before I break the night's fast, I can face with enthusiasm those copious menus of our grandfathers' days. Fruit, cereal, meat, potatoes, eggs and coffee are high spots on the list. I am not, for that matter, at all averse to oysters or clams for breakfast; fish I find most appetizing. Stews, steak, chops, all are welcome; and in smiling accord with local custom, I frequently top off breakfast with pie or cookies. And why not? I am ravenous after lugging baskets of feed, lifting full milk cans, pitching hay in the mows and breathing quantities of tingling air. Moreover, this is the meal that is to fortify me throughout the morning, hearten me for other toil ahead. Toast and a rasher of bacon would make no more impression than spit in a cloudburst.

While I am washing up in the milkhouse, I review the possibilities offered by the refrigerator and the cold pantry. If they are on the barren side, I invent dishes by combining various leftovers. If they are well stocked, I grow hungrier every minute as I weigh sausage and buckwheat cakes against steak and eggs or a thick slice of ham with a Spanish omelet. Fried potatoes with two or three soft-boiled eggs cracked over them make a fine accompaniment to calf's liver or broiled veal kidneys. Creamed codfish, with two hard-boiled eggs mashed and stirred right in, makes a festive crown to broken-up boiled potatoes. And properly fried salt pork with cream gravy on rice makes a morning to remember.

Most of the pork I consume is provided by pigs I fatten each year, then cure, and smoke over black-birch chips, or put down in brine or grind into sausage and cover with melted lard so that it will keep for a month or more. Veal kidneys and liver make infrequent appearances because I seldom fatten more than one calf for veal a year, though I do get veal kidneys from the local meat man, who gives them to me because no one will buy them! He also gives me beef kidneys, for the same reason, which go into stews that I relish at any time of day, especially when a dollop of red wine is added to the gravy.

Surprisingly enough, my breakfasts are quickly prepared. From ten to twenty minutes after I reach the warm kitchen, I can start with fruit and cereal while the main courses sizzle or bubble to perfection's peak. Seated by the kitchen's east window, I watch the sun mount above East Meadow or figure on more snow if the sky is heavy and gray. I have no possible cause to hurry. I can eat slowly while reading a book or listening to the radio. No time clock summons me, no boss can raise an eyebrow at a late arrival at the office, no last-minute sprinting is required to catch the train. And as I munch on the last bite of cookie or doughnut, I feel that the day has been well launched and that I can ride the waves till dark without a qualm.

Breakfast, I find, is enormously benefited by subsequent repose, an interim of relaxation before work begins again. So I allow myself till nine-fifteen for stretching out on the davenport in the living room for a smoke and a mental state halfway between sleep and waking. Sometimes I listen to the nine o'clock news reports; sometimes the voices, accented with the gravity of world-shaking events, reach me as faint whispers, dying as they reach my unattentive ears. But the nine-fifteen station break penetrates, not as a strident summons to duty but as a welcome bidding to the barn, where the cows will be pleased by a little attention.

So down to the cellar to stoke the furnace for the day and off to feed the few pullets that keep me in eggs, the bunnies that supply me with young fried rabbit, the pigeons that produce squabs, and whatever other livestock I may have at the time in sheds and houses. Then to the horses, which I harness, drive out to the manure wagon, hitch to it and steer back into the cow barn.

City friends, I note, tend to regard the shoveling of manure as a task offensive to eye and nose, even nauseating, a filthy, messy chore affronting the finer sensibilities. They are far from the land, however, ignorant of the value of manure. They fail to recognize it as the enriching factor that maintains soil fertility, an essential part of the cycle that makes dairying Nature's best ally.

Viewed in this light, a light that is soon sharply visible to anyone working with the land, manure is wealth, something to give thanks for. Sure, it means a messy job, but it quickly loses all offense to eye and nose. Every shovelful is regarded as a valued contribution to the soil that next year will produce lush grass and fragrant hay which the cows will eat and thus renew the cycle.

So every day for about six months of the year I load

and haul manure, and am pleased to watch the thin covering spread steadily over field after field, on top of snow most of the time, until spring arrives and the cows sally forth to partake of the young grass which they have helped to make grow.

There are something more than one hundred shovelfuls every morning to be tossed into the manure box. A manure fork is the next tool, until I can afford a manure spreader. Meanwhile, I make a game of the spreading, using a forehand stroke to the right, a backhand stroke to the left, with accuracy and dispersion as a basis for scoring points. Sometimes my backhand wins, particularly because I can get greater distance with a forkful; again a strong north wind will favor my forehand and every forkful will drop right into the chosen spot. Played that way, manure spreading is over so speedily that I almost wish the wagon held more.

No, that is exaggeration. I am glad to finish with it each morning, just as I am glad to finish with other chores. Each has its place in the daily routine and that place is better maintained no larger, no smaller. Not until along in March do I begin to weary of manure. By that time, occasional wafts of mild air hint that spring is not too far away. Then manure hauling will end. And as the end draws near, the more impatient I become to reach the end. I have been known to shorten the daily task by making a manure heap at the edge of a field instead of spreading it. I assure myself I will spread it later when the weather improves or the ground is harder, or there may be other excuses I can concoct. Sometimes I do fulfill my promise. But there are two or three heaps more than a year old in East Meadow which I do my best not to look at as I drive or walk by. They tell me all too plainly that I have been lax as a farmer.

It is at this time of year also, when winter has yet to vanish over the hills and impatience for a really hot day is at its height, that I ponder weights and measures and begin to feel sorry for myself. I recall statistics declaring that one cow during six winter months in the barn produces between eight to ten tons of manure. Therefore, with my herd, I shovel about one hundred tons of manure into the wagon between fall and spring, then spread that same enormous tonnage. I weigh in my mind the tons of grain I have helped carry off the delivery truck, dumped into the feed bin, scooped into baskets and lugged to my animals. I add some fifty tons of hay which have been hauled to the barn, forked away in the mows, forked down the chutes and finally spread before the cows. I think of the many bags of beet pulp I have lifted and dumped into baskets. And the total gets beyond my arithmetical talents, arrives at such a staggering figure of hundreds of tons that I am amazed that I have accomplished such a feat and my back creaks painfully as though the entire weight suddenly had descended on it.

At this moment I wonder if it is all worth while, if perhaps I am not deluding myself and that such herculean labor far offsets the pleasures gained.

Then my figuring takes another angle. I count up some forty pounds of hay I feed to a cow like Gaby every day, plus about ten pounds of grain, plus a few pounds of beet pulp, plus approximately fifteen gallons of water weighing some hundred and twenty pounds. The total comes to about one hundred and seventy-five pounds of food and water consumed. And out of that, Gaby has rewarded me with nearly one hundred pounds of manure and forty-to-fifty pounds of milk and managed to keep in the best of health. This I regard as miraculous, and my entire outlook changes. No longer do I feel sorry for myself. I am elated, on the contrary, for I can go right to the barn and gaze in awe at the animal that produces the miracle. Which I do.

One hour is about the average time for the manure chore, from the time I harness the horses to the final spank on their big rumps as I send them out of the barn, free for the day. Only on the foulest winter days or when the snow is really deep on the meadows do I keep them in their stalls.

Not many farmers follow this practice, but I find the horses are better for it. Unlike cows, Molly and Doc get restless in their stalls day and night with only an hour of work out of every twenty-four. Moreover, they have a resistance to cold that is phenomenal. Progressively through the fall, as the north wind sharpens, they put on heavier coats. By early spring, a slap on their flanks is like smacking a thick, dusty mattress. Throughout the winter days they roam about from meadow to meadow, all connecting gates being open; they paw away snow and nibble the dead grass, unmindful of zero temperature, even seeming to enjoy it. Only heavy, wet snowstorms, sleet or freezing rain keeps them in the barn. They are in prime condition when spring arrives; and they stand head to head to bite off each other's thick coat of hair, already beginning to shed, which I curry off whenever I have a spare moment.

With the horses out of the barn I clean their stalls,

spreading their manure in the cow drops, where it absorbs much of the cows' urine and makes their manure easier to shovel and spread.

Now comes the time for the cows to be turned out; and they are impatient for their stretch in the open, school kids waiting for the recess bell. Out they go, with a bit of deviltry from Toots or Noella, or a sudden desire by Bebop to race up and down the feed alley. Maggie is invariably last, waiting till all the others are outside before she moves, even slower than Molly. Maggie, however, knows she can do as she pleases. I delay other work while she makes up her mind that the coast is clear of all infantile monkeyshines; and then, with an arm over her back, I escort her grandly to the door, assuring her that a breath of air will be good for her. She never looks too convinced but accepts my word for it, and finally I pull the door to in back of her.

This is the daily interval when winter breeding problems are best solved. I stand at the door watching for signs of a cow being in heat.

Having watched my herd while smoking a cigarette, I climb into the hay mows and wield a pitchfork, a job I object to only in the most arctic weather. I like a hay mow, the obscurity, the fragrance. Moreover it is warming work, and despite zero readings I am soon in a glow. I heave enough hay onto the ramp for three feedings— the noon snack, the big ration in the evening and the generous breakfast portion. I shove the noon meal down the chute to the feed alley, where it finally backs up into the chute. This leaves a sufficient amount below the chute to plug it by placing a pole across the bottom. At night and after morning milking, I am hungry enough to work with dispatch and like to find all the hay I will need loose on the ramp and ready to fork down the chute in a matter of seconds.

I spread the noon hay before the stanchions and bring the cows back into the barn. They waste no time, because of the cold and the knowledge that hay awaits them. It is a pleasant time, tucking Toots into her stanchion, nudging Blondy till she leaps wildly over the gutter and into her place, keeping an eye on the wily Bebop, always ready to start a rumpus, shoving Judy past the calf pens, where she tries to stick her tongue between the palings to steal a bit of grain from their feed pans. There is rarely a morning that they fail to provide me with a good laugh.

Then I sweep the stable floor and spread lime to keep it white. This becomes a mild obsession. I care not if neighbors find the house dusted or undusted when I am alone in the winter. But the person who enters my barn and remarks, "Say, that's nice and clean," wins all my favors. Immediately I am a pushover. If he wants my shirt, he gets it—though he can't have my cows.

Livestock dealers and the vet know the value of this kind of compliment. They speak of a clean floor, a good odor; they point enviously at the fine condition of the cows, indicate a calf as exceptionally promising. And the dairyman becomes a softie, willing to accept offers or take orders which in a tougher frame of mind he would argue over bitterly. I felt like rushing out and climbing a tree out of pure joy the day Richard and I leaned over the side of my calf pen and he said, "George, you grow bigger calves than I do." Richard wasn't looking for any favors. He meant what he said. This from my whilom mentor in dairying, from one of the best dairymen in the countryside, sufficed to turn me into a babbling idiot. No sweeter praise had ever reached my ears.

With the cows satisfied for the rest of the day, I dump out the evening ration of beet pulp and pour water over it so it will have time to soak it up. I check the feed bin, heaving in a couple of bagfuls if necessary. I see if the molasses pail holds enough for Maggie and Bella. I toss a forkful or two of straw for bedding in the calf pens. I spread a few shovelfuls of sawdust where needed beneath the cows. And I close the door to the stable, then the north door to the barn, and without having to consult a watch I know that the time is 11:30 to 11:45 and that morning chores are over.

Here is the major off-duty interval for maintaining balance between leisure and labor—five full hours before evening milking starts at 5 P.M. I have worked two hours at morning milking, been free for an hour and a half, worked two hours and a half, and now have five wonderful hours to dispose of as I please. The cows are fed and happy, the barn is clean, the horses are pleased to be in the meadows, and dairying can be completely blotted from my mind if I so wish.

Barring a most untoward incident, I have no reason for concern about the barn. The worst that could happen would be the jamming of a drinking cup. Yet I would be aware of that in short order, for without thought on my part my ear would inform me that the water pump in the cellar was running more than it should and I would soon locate the trouble and remedy it. The weather holds no dreads. The house is warm, so is the barn. I may swear at a blizzard that is howling as I go to the barn in the evening; but once there with the door closed, I pay no mind to meteorological freaks without.

Storms formerly disturbed my mental tranquillity. Heavy wet snow, sleet or freezing rain in winter and flash thunderstorms in summer are likely to break power lines and disrupt electric service for periods varying from fifteen minutes to a whole day, though the latter is rare. The temporary lack of electricity in the house is of little moment. Candles and oil lamps are pleasant as a change. And I can always lug a pail of water from the spring if power is cut long enough to reduce pressure in the water tank.

But absence of power at milking time means hand milking, an art at which I seemingly will never be proficient—particularly because I, and all other dairymen, get out of practice from almost constant use of machine milkers, and cows become accustomed to the machine to such an extent that they are not as easy to milk by hand as they would be with regular hand milking. Now, however, even that worry has been put in limbo.

A stallcock, or petcock such as is used on the vacuum line, which connects with the milking machine by a rubber tube, has been threaded into the manifold on my car. When power is off I run the car into the barn, attach a length of rubber tube to the stallcock on the car engine, then to the petcock on the drain tank of the vacuum line. When I run the engine somewhat faster than idling, suction through the manifold produces vacuum in the pipe and I go merrily about my milking. It takes a little longer than when the power is on, but it saves me a couple of hours of sweaty, frustrating toil.

If I were hobby-minded I would devote my daily five hours to building ship models, tooling leather, hammering silver or stoking a pottery kiln. These crafts and many others interest me; my enthusiasm mounts to a degree of considerable warmth, but it soon slips back to the normal level and tile-making, for instance, remains in the armchair stage. As one means of sustaining the caloric phase of enthusiasm, I tell myself that such recreational enterprises frequently can be made profitable and I recall various success stories I have read about thriving businesses evolving from Grandma's recipe for sweet pickle relish or Great Uncle's talent for making milk stools, now so handy and quaint when a plethora of guests besiege the rustic abode.

Nevertheless, even the vision of wealth leaves enthusiasm tepid, if not coolish. That, of course, is the fault of the cows. As long as my bossies not only entertain me but also pay all my bills with some cash left over, I remain at a very even temperature with regard to other forms of money-making. I don't know what I would do with additional money. Even that manure spreader I yearn for will eventually be presented to me by my cows. Meanwhile I will continue to develop my forehand and backhand deliveries for manure spreading.

There is one commercial project I may get around to some day. I have a recipe for a marvelously rich and delectable *pâté* which I acquired at a Provençal manor, where I spent many enjoyable hours with its French master and mistress. The *pâté* is made of simple ingredients perfectly combined, is not at all a fussy, woman's magazine tidbit but a substantial hunk of food, and possesses an aroma that stirs tastebuds to a new burgeoning. It can be served in small cubes with cocktails and it makes a superb cold course with dinner; but the way to savor all its goodness, from the faint whiff of cognac to the delicate blending of herbs and meat, is to take a generous slice of it to a table under a tree on a summer day, eat it slowly with crusty bread and butter and a glass of wine. Olympus never knew such fare.

Here at High Meadows I could easily fatten a pig or two for the pork that goes into it; milk-fed veal would be no more of a problem, or the rabbit meat, or the chicken, or the herbs, or all the rest that goes into it. A Dutch oven would not be hard to build for the prolonged, steady heat required to cook it. I might even make the plain earthen terrines in which it is cooked. And there is no question in my mind that it would sell in a big city, especially during winter holidays. It would be expensive, I know, but mere money is too crass to have connection with such pleasure for the palate.

Until such occupations intrude, however, I manage to fill my daily five hours with little of great consequence, though never a moment drags. I read, I listen to music, I write if the mood is suitable, I take walks. Or I get comfortably propped on the davenport and do nothing—dozing, dreaming, planning projects that are most ambitious but sufficiently far in the future to induce little, if any, fatigue. One way or another, those five hours pass so quickly that I repeatedly suspect the clock of unpardonable error.

A kind of minor miracle occurs at five o'clock. No matter how enjoyably I have spent the afternoon, I am suddenly eager to go to the barn, see the cows, inquire if all has been to their liking and if they perhaps have made a little extra milk just to demonstrate their contentment. For this I am rewarded with quizzical looks and bobbing heads that bid me to cut short the nonsense and get on with serving the evening repast.

First, however, on the way to starting the evening milking, I let out a holler for Doc and Molly. Soon I hear hoofs pounding over snow and frozen ground. Doc appears at full gallop, head reared way up, tail arched and streaming, truly a thrilling spectacle. All clumsiness is gone; for a brief moment he is handsome, graceful, ready to soar like another Pegasus. But such glory is short-lived for Doc. When he slackens speed at the gate or comes upon sloping ground his long legs get tangled and slip from under him; and he tumbles ingloriously to the ground, skidding and bouncing for several yards. Once his gangly underpinning is solidly beneath him again he snorts derisively at his mishap, grins at me and leaps for the barn, where feed awaits him in his manger. Molly, far more sedate, leaves such antics to youth, plods up to me, gets her nose rubbed, then ambles slowly to her stall, just as eager for her feed as Doc is but maintaining the dignity of her age. There they remain, with plenty of hay night and morning, until liberty comes the following day.

Night milking offers more real fun than the morning job. It is the last chore of the day, something pleasant for me to contemplate. Perhaps the cows also are pleased with the thought of a long, quiet night with full bellies and more hay in muzzle's reach when they want it. In any event, they are more tranquil, more responsive.

Once the beet pulp—which to me smells like wallpaper paste, but to them is wonderfully succulent—and grain are before them, they ask to be petted and talked to, flattered as to their good looks, their nice manners and the amount of milk they let down.

I'll never be able to prove it, but I am positive that a cow is more sensitive than a woman to praise of her beauty. Gaby, beyond question, knows she is a handsome animal; and when I put an arm around her neck and tell her she is the most beautiful thing in the world, she coos and gurgles with unrestrained joy. Judy, almost as good-looking as Gaby, puts her chin on my shoulder and invites sugary compliments. Blondy, a kind of shy tom-boy type, pretends she does not care for flattery and tosses her head in refusal; but if I pass her by she lets out a shrill whoop and looks so hurt I go back to soothe her. Toots really doesn't give a damn about her looks, but she craves affection.

So night milking proceeds at customary pace; yet somehow I find more time to devote to each cow as I milk her. Penny and Blondy are a trifle slow at milking, and this permits me to dovetail petting with the spreading of bedding, forkfuls of straw and shovelfuls of sawdust, the latter helping to keep bedding in place, and preparing beet pulp for the morning. And there is always a moment for the non-milking heifers on the other side as well as the calves in their pens.

Suddenly milking is finished, hay for the night is heaped along the feed alley and in the horses' mangers, the master light switch is pulled, the barn door is closed and I am in the milkhouse.

I am not exactly a neat, orderly individual. I can

strew tobacco ashes about though ashtrays are handy. With plenty of hangers and drawers available, I manage to pile clothes on a chair till it topples over. I like to read several books at a time, permitting myself a choice according to my mood; and since I read in bed before going to sleep, books form a barricade about my bed over which I stumble every morning when I get up. But in the milkhouse neatness and orderliness are inviolate. I finally learned how much time I could save by being meticulous. Now it has developed into a mania, though uniquely in the milkhouse. There the several pails are placed in a fixed pattern on the floor; the various brushes used when the machine is disassembled are always dropped in certain places in the soapy water in the sink. Thus, when the steam is thick on a frosty morning and my glasses are bleary, I still avoid waste motion from groping for brush handles or fumbling for washcloths. I am prepared for a blindfold test any time. Since I detest the washing process, just as I detest washing dishes, the result is a minimum of time for the job. And when I close the milkhouse door my conscience is clear if I have left all within in orderliness. My stint of meticulousness has been performed for the day.

I stroll unhurriedly to the house even in inclement weather. My working day is ended. Seven o'clock has still to strike when I reach the kitchen and the evening beckons invitingly to me. Not that I am tired. On the contrary I am fresh, in the finest fettle. I have worked during three periods for a total of six and one-half hours —two each for morning and evening milking, two and a half for morning chores. The first two were separated by an interlude of an hour and a half, the second two by one of five hours—a total of six and one-half hours of leisure. The balance is perfect. Why should I be tired? The work itself has not been strenuous, and I have had ample time to rest to offset weariness. Thus the evening is a most pleasant prospect.

After living for years in Europe, especially in France, this family of three prefers a meal of several courses— not an elaborate menu requiring hours of preparation, but different dishes served separately. A soup or an *hors d'oeuvre* starts the meal, an artichoke, an avocado, various vegetables mixed with mayonnaise, asparagus, or anything else that happens to be handy—and the opportunity for invention is unlimited. Then comes a meat with a vegetable. Either a salad or a cheese, sometimes both. And dessert. With real homemade bread, baked by a neighbor, and good fresh butter.

We have a glass of wine while final touches are given to the cooking and a glass or two with dinner. As a rule this is the cheapest red wine I can buy, from California and costing $1.75 a gallon, which lasts us several days and, when I am alone, is good for a week by decanting it into carafes and smaller bottles. Also, it is every bit as good as the ordinary table wine we drank in France. The pre-dinner glass of wine provides the gentle glow of well-being and relaxation that should precede a good meal. My appetite needs no whetting, heaven knows, but the mild stimulant lends relish to every mouthful. Also it spurs on the endless arguments which Scoop and I get involved in, arguments that get whittled down to such fine points that only the dictionary or the encyclopedia can cast the deciding vote. My wife gives up early. I give up when Scoop hurls Greek and Latin at me.

When I am alone I still hold to a dinner of three and four courses. Dishes requiring long cooking are prepared during my long afternoons. A stew then merely needs reheating, which improves its flavor. A real spaghetti sauce demands two hours of slow bubbling. Made in the afternoon, it is ready in the evening at the exact moment the spaghetti has boiled to proper tenderness. All of which means that after reaching the house just before seven o'clock at night, I am ready to start eating by seven-fifteen to seven-thirty. And I continue to eat unhurriedly for close to an hour, with the radio keeping me informed on events in a world that is far beyond the ridges that hem me in.

Our eating custom, by the way, is at considerable variance with the local routine. I join with my neighbors in a substantial breakfast after milking. They, however, have a large meal—dinner—about noon, frequently the major meal of the day. I have a sandwich, a bowl of bread and milk, a salad in summer. In the evening they feed their livestock, go to the house about five-thirty for supper, a light to moderate repast, and return to the barn for milking. I decided against this schedule at the very start. I dislike eating in a hurry; and if anything would give me indigestion, it would be the thought of rushing to work in the barn immediately after eating in the evening. So I rebelled, remained impervious to jokes at my expense, and began milking at five P.M., a full hour before my neighbors.

I feed the cows and start milking before they have finished eating, though the textbooks say a cow lets down her milk faster if she is not eating. My cows, ignorant of textbooks, milk out just as fast whether they are eating or not. And by the time I have finished the first one, the others have lapped up the last speck of feed before them. When I have finished milking, I am ravenous for food and can enjoy it because work is ended. The fact that my cows are milked at intervals of eleven hours by day and thirteen hours by night doesn't bother them in the least. They simply give more milk in the morning than at night.

My after-dinner diversions are radio, if the program promises entertainment, and reading, unless neighbors drop in, though that is rare, and it is even rarer that I hie myself forth. By nine-thirty I am in bed, again with a book, and by ten o'clock lights are out.

CHAPTER 14

I DON'T SEEK TO GIVE THE IMPRESSION THAT I am like the Englishman who invariably manages to transport a good share of London into the heart of the jungle or the desert or wherever he chances to be stationed. On the other hand, I find no reason for my turning completely rustic and adopting new habits just because they conform with local ideas. I have lived differently from my farmer neighbors, and it seems best that I continue to live differently, as long as such differences are private and not in conflict with my surroundings.

This caused me some concern at first. I wondered if I would be looked upon as a "city guy," a kind of pariah receiving a curt nod of recognition here and there but never a bid for friendship. Such fears proved to be nonsensical. In fact, I am now convinced that the one attitude on my part that probably would have closed doors to me would have been that of trying to be very rural.

Everyone knew I was from the city. They expected me to be different. Any camouflage on my part might well have been disastrous insofar as friendly relationships were concerned. These people were not to be talked up to or talked down to. I had to meet them directly, on a mutual level.

I got something of the key to the situation when I met a local doctor.

"What do you do?" he asked.

"I'm a farmer."

"What? No farmer ever had a moustache like yours," he barked back.

My moustache is a fair-sized growth and the ends turn up slightly, contrary to the local fashion for the few moustaches encountered. Well, I could have taken the remark as an insult, which wouldn't have got me very far; I could have attempted a lame apology, which would have been just as bad; or I could counter as any native would do.

"Change that to 'No moustache ever had a farmer like me,'" I answered, "and I'll agree."

He laughed. "Okay with me."

And in another minute we were talking about New York and the fun he hoped to have at an approaching convention there. We get along fine.

The good farmer of today, like his village brothers, is intelligent, shrewd and well informed. He reads newspapers and magazines, listens to broadcasts, and has definite opinions on local, state, national and international affairs. Generally speaking, he is conservative in his thinking; yet he is tolerant, ready to listen to arguments against his opinions, though it takes a powerful argument to change his mind. He gets around, he knows cities, and with nothing very positive against them he prefers his own open fields and the countryside which he knows so intimately. The era of the hayseed, the clodhopper, the rube, is long past, at least in these parts.

Today's farmer is a man of the world, remarkably capable and resourceful in a dozen skilled trades. I'll match him against the average city man any time, with odds on the farmer. And as friendship grows there apparently is no limit to the services and kindnesses he and his wife and his children will render.

Friendly neighbors are important in the country, perhaps not vital to a hermit's existence but otherwise valuable. I like seclusion but I am no hermit; so slowly I have come to know quite a few people, though I still have difficulty getting their names straight. I like to be part of the community; I find it reassuring, good for the spirit. Moreover, I have absorbed a fund of information through conversation, especially on dairying from men like Richard, information that went far toward smoothing my early and very bumpy road.

Now I believe I have proved a hope, rather than a conviction, that had long been in my mind. I have established to my satisfaction that a combination can be worked out and made practical, a combination of city habits and viewpoints with a livelihood in the country. Actually, the only urban offering I miss, and regret, is the theater. Otherwise, I enjoy all the good music I can listen to with records and FM radio. (I find a pertinent commentary on modern rural life in the fact that Rural Radio Network, with FM broadcasts in New York State and eastern Pennsylvania, transmits almost the entire daily schedule of WQXR, a station in New York which is unsurpassed for music programs.) I have plenty of books—some of which I continue to read again and again, others of current publication that arrive from one source or another. I have the few magazines I care for to keep me in touch with literary trends, art developments and general topics, plus—and I gladly pay the compliment— the remarkable Sunday edition of The New York *Times*, which capably presents a weekly round-up of just about everything happening in the world. I have farm bulletins and magazines for new ideas in the work that pays my bills.

Along with such bone and sinew for a pleasant life is the daily rhythm on which I have dwelt at some length. Instead of looking eagerly forward to an annual vacation of three short weeks, I frequently wonder if I am not on vacation a good share of the year. With enough work —enthralling work, moreover—to fill in the empty parts of each day, I have almost more leisure than I can cope with; for despite my proclivity for the horizontal position and a slothful tendency I am not totally stranger to bursts of activity. Also, I am in the country, where countless vacationists congregate for their long-awaited repose. But I am no longer a transient; I am in my own countryside, on my own land, free to walk over my own meadows, through my own woods.

The real vacation starts late in July. The strenuous haying season winds up about July 15; and from then till the middle of October, when the cows start staying in the barn at night, my work is reduced to a minimum: two daily milkings, with only a small amount of grain to scoop out for the milkers and perhaps fifteen minutes to clean the barn any time during the morning that pleases me—two hours and a half for everything. That's the daily schedule for three months. Odd jobs, "tinkering," occasional spells in the vegetable garden are welcome for variety, like tennis or golf at some resort. Otherwise I am free.

From spring to fall, friends arrive for a day, a week end, or longer. That is when long evenings are most rewarding. Milking is over about half past six; the cows are out, decorating the green slopes with patterns of black and white. As in the city, I can have a hot shower or, as not in the city, I can go to the milkhouse and slosh about in cold spring water. As in the city I change clothes, slacks for dungarees, a fresh shirt, moccasins for work shoes. While others have cocktails, which they usually prefer, I have my glass of clean, dry wine under the crabapple tree, in the grape arbor, or just lying about on the lawn.

Dinner may be as late as eight o'clock while daylight holds, for there is no hurry, nobody is going anywhere, there's no place to go. If the delay calls for an extra glass of wine, so much the better. Fate is kind. Then the leisurely dinner lasts till well after dark. High Meadows is always favored with a light breeze, and chance mosquitoes are wafted on their way. Fireflies mount and nosedive in their nightly amorous acrobatics. And when talk subsides, the intimate quiet of the country envelops us all.

To me, this is gracious living, richer than anything in my past experience, even in Europe, even in France where gracious living is an art. Yet it is neither lavish nor expensive. We are not wealthy, not by a long shot.

Guests contribute a share of the provender, a big steak perhaps, a gallon of olive oil, a well-fed turkey. Drinks other than wine are left to them. They are surer of cocktails if they bring their own gin. What with products from the garden, and the farm itself, I doubt if our food bills for our most costly summer weeks amount to more than forty dollars, for the food is simple, relying on preparation rather than price for its excellence. By contrast, when I am alone during the winter, I do handsomely on about ten dollars.

Now I should revise the almost ultra-conservative estimate of income from a herd of twelve milking Holsteins. A yearly average of 8,000 pounds of milk per cow is not exceptional; 12,000 pounds could be classed as exceptional; 10,000 pounds is the figure to strive for and plenty of superior-grade Holsteins can achieve it. A daily average of thirty-five pounds for a ten-month lactation period suffices. Twelve cows producing at that rate make a total of 120,000 pounds of milk a year. In 1950 the average price paid in this locality per hundredweight of milk was better than $3.50. For 1951 the average will be above $4.00 and probably will not decline for the next few years. However, still on the conservative side, figure on $3.75. That makes an annual gross return of $4,500.00.

Experience with cows does not take long to reveal means for economizing in the management of a herd, especially in feeding, the major item of expense. Such efficiency should assure a net income of approximately sixty per cent of gross or, on the above total, $2,750. This is just about the figure I will reach for 1951, when for the first time I am milking twelve cows. I would have attained that goal much sooner had I started with twelve cows; but I count it sufficient that fate introduced me to enough cows to start dairying—and the intervening years, not lost in any sense, have been fascinating. Allowing $250.00 annually for a new seeding of eight to ten acres—lime, fertilizer, a long-lasting legume such as birdsfoot trefoil, and a nurse crop of oats for the first year—the remaining $2,500.00 is spendable income.

Again I admit this is not munificence. Jewels and mink coats are hardly to be found therein, though a few luxuries might be squeezed out by careful budgeting. But for a steady, reliable income from farming I question if, work and all included, it can be equalled. At any rate, it permits us to live as described above.

Balance always recurs to me as the dominant factor in my new life. It figures prominently or subtly in every moment and act. Each season is lived fully. The tribulations of winter are forgotten in the lazy heat of summer. The rebirth of spring is lost in the dying of autumn. Weeks of haying are offset by three months of loafing. Brief summer chores merely add zest to pleasant evenings. And an interval of toil is followed by an interval of leisure. This is, moreover, no delicate balance, easily thrown over. Based on Nature, on the land, it stands solid against adversity. It may sway when ill winds blow hardest, but nothing short of a cataclysm could topple it.

Cows, in my opinion, are the essential counterpoise assuring this balance. Their ability to make milk out of grass and hay removes the hazard that is inevitable in other types of farming. Weather that can wreak havoc with crops can at the worst spoil only a part of my hay;

and, if I run short of hay during the winter, the fortnightly milk check is steady income that will pay for hay while other expenditures are held down. Fluctuating market prices may mean a fat income from crops one year, a very lean one the next, especially for the small farm unable to store crops until prices rise. The price of milk sold to the New York milkshed also fluctuates, on a seasonal basis; the price to the farmer is lowest during the flush period of late spring, highest in midwinter. But the dairyman's producing costs are lowest in late spring and highest in midwinter so that the monetary return per pound of milk holds fairly stable.

Milk, moreover, has no substitute. City folks can get along with substitutes for virtually everything but milk —potatoes for other vegetables, beef instead of pork, or pork instead of beef, even fish instead of meat, one fruit instead of another—but they could hardly survive without milk. Yet milk production constantly lags behind demand, and the day appears to be far in the future when city markets will be glutted with milk. This assures at least a fair price for milk to the dairyman.

Milk thus strikes me as unique among farm products. It has no substitute or ever will have one. Cows also, to me, are unique. They have no substitute in the animal world. Along with the income they provide me, they offer companionship, affection and an unending round of diversion—hilarious entertainment along with spells of exasperating stubbornness or wilfulness which, however, reveal no trace of meanness, but rather such a profound innocence that I cannot hold anything against them. Thus the cow possesses exceptional balance. She offers the whole gamut of emotions, and in return for good care and feed she guarantees my living.

My cows have done better than that. Money, in the sense of cash in the pocket to pay the butcher, the baker and all the others on the long list of bills due, hardly enters my mind any more. It is as though from those sleek black-and-white bodies with their smooth, rounded udders, not only milk flows for me but also beefsteaks, hams, potatoes, artichokes, shoes, dungarees, sweatshirts and everything else I need. The gap between having and not having, formerly bridged, precariously or not, only by money, now has been closed. Money is no longer necessary. In return for the milk checks I receive I sign other similar bits of paper, as checks, and in return obtain everything essential to good living. When money loses its meaning as an elusive, yet vital necessity, a medium to be struggled for, worried over, feared when possessed for spending, and even more feared when not possessed; when money becomes a scrap of paper which I sign, then I feel free.

So I say, "Hail the Holstein." The cow is a wonderful animal, a loving and lovable triumph of evolution that has achieved the ultimate in the social scheme. Provide her with a living and she provides you with a living. To her a long and echoing toast—in milk.

INDEX

Index